Paths of Light

Also by John Stewart Collis

SHAW
FORWARD TO NATURE
FAREWELL TO ARGUMENT
THE SOUNDING CATARACT
AN IRISHMAN'S ENGLAND
AN ARTIST OF LIFE

WHILE FOLLOWING THE PLOUGH
DOWN TO EARTH
THE TRIUMPH OF THE TREE
THE MOVING WATERS

Paths of Light

by

JOHN STEWART COLLIS

CASSELL · LONDON

CASSELL & COMPANY LTD

35 Red Lion Square . London WC1

and at

MELBOURNE · SYDNEY · TORONTO · CAPETOWN
JOHANNESBURG · AUCKLAND

———

Printed in Great Britain by
Ebenezer Baylis and Son, Limited, The
Trinity Press, Worcester, and London
F. 459

Contents

		Page
VIEWPOINT		vii

PART I LIGHT

CHAPTER 1 THE NEW ALCHEMY

i	The Modern Discovery	3
ii	The Atom	5
iii	The Atom within the Atom	9
iv	The Bonds	13
v	The New Alchemy	17
vi	The Sun	21

CHAPTER 2 THE NATURE OF LIGHT

i	What is Light?	28
ii	The Mills of God	30
iii	Colours	35
iv	The Wonderland	40
v	Sky Colours	43
vi	The Rainbow	47
vii	Fire	49

CHAPTER 3 REFLECTIONS AND ILLUSIONS

i	Reflections	54
ii	The Bubble	57
iii	The Drop	61
iv	The Mirage	63

CHAPTER 4 PHOSPHORESCENCE

i	In the Mineral	68
ii	In the Air	71
iii	In the Plant	74
iv	In the Animal	76
v	In the Sea	80

v

PART II MAN AND LIGHT

Page

CHAPTER 1 THE STORY OF THE LAMP

    i   Lighting   87

   ii   Sins Against Light   97

CHAPTER 2 OPENING WINDOWS

    i   The Coming of Glass   105

   ii   Glass and Civilization   108

  iii   The Window of the Telescope   111

  iv   The Window of the Microscope   115

CHAPTER 3 SUN-WORSHIP

    i   Sun-Gods   122

   ii   The Sun as Saviour   125

  iii   Solar Relics   129

  iv   The Scientific Approach   132

CHAPTER 4 SCIENCE AND
             IMAGINATION

    i   Newton and the Poets   136

   ii   Blake and Wordsworth   139

  iii   Keats and the Rainbow   144

  iv   Science and Imagination   146

   v   Goethe's Attack on Newton   152

  vi   Enlightened Men   166

BIBLIOGRAPHY   171

INDEX   175

VIEWPOINT

OVER ten years ago now I was standing in a field on a lovely October day, with a plough and a tractor. It was time to knock off, but I was not pleased on that account. I was in the South-West of England, in the heart of a farm, tucked away from roads and traffic. The field was a fifteen-acre of stubble on a considerable rise. Woods surrounded it, but from the highest point I could see across the trees to further fields, looking very trim, and bulging as if blown up with air from beneath. One of them, forked and edged by a layer of chalk, resembled a pair of brown trousers spread upon a sheet. From the clump of trees on my left came the roofless oratory of the rooks, and below, the talking water of the hidden stream. The leaves that had died with summer's ending had come to life again and the crests of the silver birches were now gold. I had ploughed my stubble all day in preparation for drilling with winter wheat. Sea-gulls had followed in the furrows of my falling waves of earth. The coulters of my plough, which had started rusty, now gleamed in the light after contact with the epitome of perfect cleanliness. And from the overturned sods that cold whiff came up to me, that odour which emanates health and strength and eternal life. I was sorry the day's work was done, and would gladly have continued for a few more hours turning the stubble; and I thought how good it would be to live out my whole life in the convent of the sequestered fields.

Circumstances did not make this possible; and in any case there was something I wanted to do more. I wanted to give a view of natural phenomena *as a whole* from the focal point of a man standing in a field. I wanted to connect the sciences.

'All the sciences are so bound together,' said Descartes, 'that it is much easier to learn them all at once than to learn one alone by detaching it from the others.' I do not like detached lumps of knowledge—meteorology, for instance, detached from geology, or botany from physics. I do not much like 'knowledge for its own sake'. I want it for the sake of a vision of the whole. I want it for the sake of art—and why should the arts be separated from the sciences any more than the sciences from one another?

Since Nature is almost another word for interrelatedness our habit of parcelling things up for the sake of convenience is unfortunate. If we stand in a field, as it were, and see all the phenomena as one thing, we get a better idea of the relationship and can gather the threads together. I have already made a start with this, connecting the threads concerning trees, and water, and other things—including the glorious work of man himself on the fields.[1] Even so I have been obliged to take much 'as given'. I have taken the sun as given. I have said nothing about light, nothing about why the grass is green, nothing about how we come to be able to see the grass. This is what I must do now—connect Light with the scheme. That means that I must introduce the sun. But I cannot deal with the constitution of the sun or the ways of light without reference to physics. It may be rash for me to say this in a foreword and thus risk a hastily shut book by the very readers I would reach. For though a certain amount of nature-study from botany and geology is allowed to be a 'literary subject', there is a fixed idea that physics is outside our pale, like mathematics. This is most

[1] In: *While Following the Plough*
Down to Earth
The Triumph of the Tree
The Moving Waters

unfortunate, for we are all physicists these days, glibly using phrases about H-bombs and atoms and nuclear fission as if we understood the matter. We do not reverently apply the imaginative, poetic, religious portion of our minds to this study, regarding it as harsh and grating. Yet it is my plan to start with an attempt to reveal that physics is neither alien to our understanding nor our imagination. Then we can come to the sun and to light and what we ourselves make of it, including—and this I never like to omit—an anthropological glance backward to those days when man, while being wrong about the facts, was rather more aware of significance than we are. I aim to deal with those aspects which are not too technical. Some may be of minor importance, but I do not think that anything in the whole of Nature is more worth imaginative attention than the fundamental miracle of the action of sunlight with the green vegetable cells which may properly be called the mills of God.

PART I

Light

CHAPTER ONE

The New Alchemy

i

THE MODERN DISCOVERY

WE look out upon the world and we see the firm ground beneath our feet, the weighty mountains, the waters, the skies, the plants, the animals, and the human race. There is a difference, we notice, between the plants and any piece of solid ground—the plants get up and they fall down. They possess a force of some sort: whereas we never see a rock swell and shrink in this manner. We notice that animals have the power not only to grow but to move. It is the same with ourselves: we can lift our arms: we can go about —in answer to a principle of energy. We observe another force at work—the strong strokes of the wind. We see another—the power of water as it flows or falls. And another—fire leaping from object to object. And again—a tree struck down by a flash of lightning.

So much has been obvious to man since before the beginning of history: on the one hand the solid, inanimate earth; and on the other, Force disclosing itself as motion in the growing plant and the moving creature, in wind, water, electricity, and the consuming fire.

From the dawn of history men were aware of these powers, and as time went on they began to add the force of wind and water to the energy of their arms. Then they went a step farther and used fire, and farther still and used the swifter combustion of gases, and at the same time were enabled to channel the currents of electricity. There they stopped.

They stopped there until only the other day. If we pass in review all the civilizations which have risen and fallen since the first records, we see that not one of them, and not our own civilization until about half a century ago, knew that more energy was to be found elsewhere. After all, why should there be? The universe was getting on all right. It didn't need any more force, and in any case there was nowhere to look for it.

This was an error, as everyone now knows. There is force in reserve. There is force deposited in a bank, as it were. That bank is matter. It is now known that matter is not inanimate, that it is not inert, that it is not lifeless. The material composing the mountain, the lake, the air, is made up of cages imprisoning lions and tigers.

This is the great modern discovery—with which nothing can compete. It was not astonishing to find that the moon is rather more than twenty miles away, and that the stars are larger than sixpenny pieces. It was not astonishing to learn the facts about combustion, magnetism, electricity, or gravitation, since they openly declared themselves; but it is astonishing to discover that this stone which I hold in my hand is not a solid but a conglomeration of cages, each with a tiger inside. I put it that way because I see it that way, and I need strong words, though those words are too weak and none could be obedient enough to do justice to the full truth, and I am amazed at the indifferent manner in which people today accept as a matter of course the discoveries of nuclear physics. It is as if there were a determination in modern times *not* to regard the mysteries of the world as mysteries, and to discourage any movement of the imagination. It is allowed that a 'heavenly vision' may come to mystics and seers from the view on the mountain-top, but a like vision is not supposed to follow from a view of the less easily discernible lands of the nuclei where nevertheless the builder has laid the foundations of empire. Physics is not supposed to be a religious or a poetic study. I cannot share this view, and I confess that ever since I looked into the subject hardly a day has passed as I have gone about that I have not increasingly marvelled at the masonry of creation and the mystery of design. Dr. George Gamow, celebrated physicist and delightful writer, when writing his book on the sun, found himself obliged to devote some space to physics. He apologizes for this. 'The author regrets the pain that this excursion into the domain of pure physics may cause some readers who picked up this book for its astronomical title,' he says, 'but except for poets, no one should speak about stars without knowing the properties of matter of which they are constructed.'[1] I am sorry he said that about poets. If such knowledge is to be considered too stiff for those who make the poetic approach to reality, then the absurd position may yet be reached when science can give nothing to poetry and poetry nothing to science.

ii

THE ATOM

Let us take the nearest thing that comes to hand—a stone. Until roughly a hundred years ago in spite of the penetrating deduction of Democritus among the non-

[1] *The Birth and Death of the Sun.*

experimenting Greeks, it had been generally believed that such a piece of matter was a continuous whole, as you might think of a slab of jelly; and that theoretically you could divide it up into ever smaller and smaller and smaller pieces. It was not till the middle of the nineteenth century that the discovery was made (by Dalton) that matter is already divided up, and is not like a slab of jelly but a packet of peas. These peas were regarded as final, and called atoms, after the Greek—'that which cannot be divided'.

The scientists then set to work to find out what they could about these atoms, and soon ascertained that they were not all the same size nor all the same make. Their size differed no more than apples on an apple tree, but some of them differed from others so much that if a sufficient number of a similar lot were bunched together to become visible, you saw gold, while another lot would give you mercury. It was found that there were ninety-two different sorts (a few more were added later) and these were now named the Elements—thus disposing of the old time-honoured idea that there were just four fundamental elements, Fire, Earth, Air, and Water. The reason why we see so many more substances in the world than ninety-two is because the different sorts of atoms combine as molecules to make a great variety of compounds, the most famous example being when two atoms of hydrogen join with one atom of oxygen to give us something quite different from either, which we call water: while a more complicated example of atomic building would be, say, Socrates.

Their minuteness offers a pictorial challenge. 'No such things as atoms?' said Rutherford. 'Why, I can see the little beggars!' But that is just our difficulty; we cannot see them, nor can any ordinary microscope, and we are obliged to be content with the utterances of those who can make formidable mathematical calculations. Thus we are told that the number of atoms necessary to cover the space on a speck of dust would be some thousand million million— 1,000,000,000,000,000 atoms perched on a speck of dust. Take two more examples. Remembering that a molecule of water equals three atoms, 'The number of molecules in a little drop of water', says Gamow, 'is about the same as the number of drops of water in the great Lake Michigan.' And this from the accomplished writer as well as physicist, Professor E. N. da C. Andrade: 'If a staff of a thousand men were told off to count the atoms in a single one of the little bubbles of gas which collect on the side of a glass of soda-water, and if each man could count three hundred atoms a minute, and counted twelve hours a day all the year round, the job would take a million years.' That seems strange to me. It is almost saying that there is no limit to smallness. I find it easier to imagine no limit to bigness. There must be a point when something becomes nothing, and one cannot help feeling that some things would have become no things before a thousand million million of them could find room on a speck of dust. Is it a myth? Is it a fairy tale to end all fairy tales? Are we to trust our scientists more than the Schoolmen of old who debated on how many angels could balance on the point of a needle? We are inclined to ask such questions in our surprise; yet we are bound to acknowledge that we are scarcely entitled to use the word myth in this connexion. A myth is something which is not objectively true. The fairies were not objectively true, the host of primitive gods were not objectively true, they were mythical, and in consequence though you prayed to them and performed rituals in their honour and made sacrifices to them, you could never count upon their doing what you asked, since unfortunately they did not exist. Our scientists are on firmer ground. They say there is a genie in the bottle. If we say—Nonsense, there is no bottle and no genie, they can uncork it and let out a monster who in a few minutes can destroy a city. But this is anticipating—we are bound to accept atoms and a lot of them, so perhaps it does not matter if we accept a greater number than we can conceive.

We do see atoms whenever they are bunched together in sufficient numbers to show us a substance; but as we cannot see them individually we find it hard to realize that they are all *in motion*.[1] They are all dedicated to eternal activity: unpausingly they pursue an endless path and revolve in ceaseless chase—in the gas, in the liquid, in the solid. It is as if matter were composed of untold numbers of swarming insects. We can accept this as we walk through a gas, since they are then free from one another; we can accept it as we swim through water, since they are then fairly free; but how about the stone wall—surely there they are so clamped together that they have come to rest? Yet no, even there they are pushing and pulling, quivering, squirming, vibrating, struggling—for solids are by no means solid. We should really expect this activity on the part of atoms, for motion is Energy made manifest, and atoms are the immediate ministers of Energy. Yes, we may say, we can accept that, but accustomed as we are to think of nature in terms of mighty opposites such as light with darkness, heat with cold, noise with silence and so on, should we not find the opposite to motion, which would be perfect stillness? Yet we are told that it is not in the solid, not in the corpse, not in the tomb. Is there then no standstill? There is: but we can only find it in a temperature of 273 degrees below the freezing point of ice—when the very air itself would be concrete block.

[1] Known as the Brownian Movement.

iii

THE ATOM WITHIN THE ATOM

For a decade the scientific world was content, in general, to accept atoms as final in themselves—as indivisible particles, solid as billiard balls. I say in general, for some, especially Clerk Maxwell, were not prepared to accept it save under protest. For if the doctrine of evolution were true and Nature proceeded by process of steady building and change, how could the foundation bricks consist of lifeless, change-less particles? And how on earth could they cling together and form wholes? Nevertheless it did not appear to trouble people very much, and it seems to have been accepted as quite in order by the main body of scientists and laymen alike.

Then came the great day when one of the elements was discovered to be buzzing with *interior* activity. It was found to be pouring particles out of itself at a terrific speed, rather like a volcano in eruption, or as if we had come upon a rock which turned out to be a fort firing into the open. Such a fort could not be solid, it must contain room for guns, ammunition, and soldiers. This was the element of uranium thus found to be so active—or radioactive as we now say. It was immediately deduced that if one element were like this the other elements probably possessed equally interest-ing interiors. At once Rutherford said, in effect: 'We must penetrate the other atoms. How can we do this? We cannot unscrew them with a tweezers, we cannot split them open with a knife—but we can take a gun and shoot at them. And what better gun can we use than a radioactive sub-stance, and what better bullets than the particles shooting

9

out at almost the speed of light?' A good idea. We can all have good ideas. 'Do you think highly of *Gulliver's Travels*, Dr. Johnson?' someone asked. 'Why, sir,' he replied, 'when once you have thought of big men and little men, it is very easy to do all the rest.' Yet of course the truth is the opposite to this. We can all think of big men and little men, and all fail to do anything with them. That is the history of failed artists and scientists and inventors the world over. It is not the history of Rutherford, the great Rutherford, whose largeness and geniality loom even in every text-book which mentions his name. He took the gun and fired with the alpha particles (as they were called to distinguish them from two other rays that also came out) at atoms in his laboratory at Cambridge. Nothing happened. He fired again. Nothing happened. He fired again, a machine-gun fire of ten thousand bullets. Nothing happened. He had shot at ghosts. He persevered—and suddenly one of the particles hit something and bounced away. From that moment, we may say, the door was open and a thorough-going examination of the interior of the atom became possible.

I will set down the relevant facts: they can be stated quite briefly without doing violence to the complexities which we accept as a matter of course. One point ought to be made clear first. The layman is, I think, inclined to be a little misled about one thing by the scientists, on account of their terminology. They speak of the 'rim' of the atom, and the 'shells' of the atom, and the 'flesh' of the atom, not to mention the 'splitting' of the atom, as if it were a ball or a box with a lid or a covering. But is it like a box that you can open? or an onion that you can peel? or a fleshy oyster with a pale poetic pearl for prize? By no means. Its boundary consists of whirling electrified particles—which alone are responsible for 'rims' or 'shells'. The following is all that need be said at the moment about the structure of the atom. It contains a central core round which other particles circle at the speed of several thousand million million revolutions a second. They travel in a circle because they are attracted by this central nucleus rather as the earth is attracted by the sun, but not for the same reason. The attraction here is electrical; for the machinery of the universe is largely governed by the fact that one of its fundamental forces, electricity, attracts and repels itself by virtue of two mani-festations of itself. One of these manifestations we call positive and the other negative, though the terms are as arbitrary as if they had been called male and female, there being nothing more negative about the negative charge than the positive. In fact both are extremely positive in this —that a positive charge repels a positive charge and a negative a negative, while a positive attracts a negative and a negative a positive, and the attraction is so enormously greater than that of gravitation as to promote general harmony and stability in the architecture of matter. The central core, or nucleus, or atom within the atom, is posi-tively charged with particles called protons while the encircling particles called electrons are negatively charged, and being much lighter would certainly be drawn into the centre were it not for their excessive speed. This speed also serves to clear a space round the nucleus and prevents other atoms from coming too near, for it creates a kind of rim or round wall, and the orbit of this wall defines the size of the atom. In the main this will pass as the model for all atoms from the simplest hydrogen atom with one proton balancing one electron, to uranium with ninety-two of each, though extra neutralized particles called neutrons generally add further weight to the nucleus.

Two more facts of interest arise from this structure.

First, practically all the weight of the atom resides within the nucleus. It takes millions of nuclear particles to occupy a cubic inch, but that cubic inch would weigh a billion times as much as a cubic inch of water—that is about ten million tons. I take that figure from Hecht. Gamow formulated, with practical success, the theory that different nuclei may be considered as the minute droplets of a universal 'nuclear fluid', and he calculated that one cubic centimetre of it would weigh two hundred and forty million tons. So we are in fairyland again: at least not the land we experience where a pound of sugar is quite a large object.

The second fact of interest is that the volume of space kept clear by the electrons is enormously greater than the total volume of the electrons themselves—the ratio being that of bullets in a battle-field. The nucleus, though very heavy, is very small—less than a single electron. Thus the space between the orbit and the nucleus is so large as to justify the comparison that, say, the six electrons in the atom of carbon are like six wasps in Waterloo Station—with a fly in the middle representing the nucleus. No wonder Rutherford was obliged to fire ten thousand bullets before he hit his target.

Thus we see that a solid is not solid but chiefly holes; and water also full of holes; and the air riddled with holes. It would be interesting to be able to make practical demonstrations of this, for if we could empty the emptiness out of an elephant it would shrink to much less than the size of a mouse; indeed, they say that if the Empire State Building in New York were thus treated it would lodge comfortably on the head of a pin—though it would not be easy for us to pick up the pin-head since it would weigh tens of thousands of tons. It is not easy for us to realize the essential hollowness of things, that we are all hollow men. We see a great hulk of material in front of us and we suppose that it is massive because of its material. Yet it is massive because it lacks material; it is bulky because it has little bulk; it is visible because most of it does not exist. This is not immediately obvious. But if we make a pyramid of empty petrol-tins and then squash them together leaving no hollowness, we would see a remarkable shrinkage of the pile. How much more if we squash together the millions and millions of tiny hollows in every thousandth of an inch of material. The truth is that emptiness is the norm of the universe. It is almost void of matter. We think of the constellations of the heavens and of the countless stars in the uncounted galaxies. Yet a cosmic ray travelling at the speed of light for ten thousand million years is unlikely to traverse as much matter as would cover a two-shilling piece. Jeans offers the pictorial analogy that six specks of dust in Waterloo Station represent the extent to which space is populated with stars. If we turn our gaze from the unspeakable amplitude of the sky to the minute particulars of the earth and remember those six wasps in Waterloo Station as representing six electrons in the atom of carbon, we begin to realize that though the universe is big the difficulty is to find anything in it.

iv

THE BONDS

Yet—has it not been said?—'Where there is Nothing there is God.' We do not understand the mystery of Nothingness. We cannot grasp the creativity of emptiness. 'Clay is fashioned, and thereby the pot is made; but it is its hollow-

13

ness that makes it useful,' said the great mystic, Meister Eckhart. 'By cutting out doors and windows the room is formed; it is the space which makes the room's use. So that when things are useful it is that in them which is Nothing which makes them useful.' All we know is that when we contemplate the universal void, the fields of space, the ever-lasting horizons of unlimited nothingness, certain Mani-festations, which we call life and matter, appear before our eyes. Given the delicate labours of the physicists it is the privilege of modern man to behold the bricks which have been appointed for the foundation of the earth. If from the mountain-top we can sometimes be lifted up in spirit as we survey the finished figures, our elation need not be less when we look down and mark their masonry.

There are the ninety-two elements. We must not think of them, and we do not think of them, as sitting in a row in-dependent of one another and sufficient unto themselves. They combine. Just as the twenty-six letters of the alphabet, which on their own are not much good, are combined to give us words and all the wonder of words, so the ninety-two elements (or most of them) combine to give us the wonders of the world. The question is—why do they com-bine, and how do they cohere?

How do they manage to stick together? The packet of peas, as it were, should spill all over the place. There is no glue holding them in position. If we shatter a stone we can-not bring the pieces together again. Many answers to this question were advanced at first. Some experts held that the atoms had claws or brackets, others said that they possessed a sort of spear with which they hooked each other, while yet others maintained that they came together because they loved one another, and we were given what might fairly be called the love-life of atoms. We smile, but I think we must agree that attraction, magnetism, affinity, love, such as we think of in human terms need not be denied roots reaching back into the abyss of time. Still, to use the word 'love' here would lead us straight into superficial mystification and not in the least into profound mysticism. Let us use the right words in the right places. The right word here is 'electricity'—by no means to be equated with Spirit.

It is electricity which is mainly responsible for bringing the atoms together and for holding them in place; and it is the electrons—ridden as it were by electricity like a jockey on a horse—which are the agents of combination and cohesion. Again let us consider the ninety-two elements. If we make a list of them and arrange it according to weight and electronic number from the simplest to the most complex, we will notice that the most stable elements appear at mathematically regular intervals and possess certain attributes, and for this reason we call our list the Periodic Table. All the elements are not stable. Many are in danger of breaking down if left to themselves, of losing their identity, and the more complicated they are in their rings or shells of electrons, the more liable they are to disintegrate like uranium and radium at the far end of the Table, which cannot preserve their integrity and wither into lumps of heavy hopeless lead. 'The overcrowding in these radioactive elements', says Bertrand Russell in an artless sentence, 'must be something awful. No wonder they are in a hurry to leave such a slum.'[1] The element of silver which comes in the middle of the Table is said to occupy the place of greatest stability, and it seems that if there were more instability among the other elements the whole earth would be made of silver. Apart from this, those elements which occur in set periods are so much more stable and independent that

1 *The ABC of Atoms.*

they are called Noble or Inert Gases, all of which except one possess the important property of eight electrons in their outer rings. Now there is such virtue in this number eight (I am sorry it is not seven) that all the other elements strive towards the octet so as to achieve stability. They manage this by joining forces and exchanging electrons or, if need be, sharing them. Thus it is easy to see that lithium with only one electron in its outer shell will readily combine with fluorine, which having seven needs one, and so both are satisfied in their search for stability, for both in combination have achieved the octet; that when an oxygen atom, which needs two electrons, takes them from beryllium which has two to spare, then both are satisfied in their search for stability, for both have achieved the octet; that when an atom of sodium which needs to get rid of one electron in order to become like the Noble Gas neon, exchanges it with chlorine which needs one more in order to become like the Noble Gas argon, so that together they form a molecule of an entirely new property called salt, then both are satisfied in their search for stability, for both have achieved the octet.

I lay down the general principle which we can all understand, without the blur of modification and with no attempt even to suggest the detail of the dance of the electrons, of the electrical ballet in the orbits of all shapes and sizes from swelling circle to narrowest ellipse, from solitary path to crowded causeway, for neither the imagination, the eye, nor the microscope can help us to do justice to the reality. The notable thing is that though the electrons move round their orbits about seven thousand million times in the millionth of a second, and we should expect endless collision and hopeless chaos, there is instead the beauty and rest of perfect symmetry.

Thus the elements are drawn together in fraternal embrace in every kind of combination from simple to elaborate forms, and we get the world we know. We get more—for we promote further assemblies ourselves. We create more world. This comprises the achievement of chemistry, revealing the power of man to understand the movements and anticipate the needs of the elements. When we think of this, when we contemplate the work of these architects who build with invisible bricks, we feel that man with all his faults, with all his clay, his mud, and his madness, has truly in him, as Nietzsche said, 'the creator and the sculptor, the hardness of the hammer, the divine blessedness of the spectator on the seventh day.' But my main concern, the main point which I have reached at last, is the fact that this interlocking of the outer electrons of atoms serves to forge very powerful *bonds*.

v

THE NEW ALCHEMY

It is not easy to break these bonds. If they are cast asunder, if they are snapped, as you might snap a taut piece of elastic, or wound-up spring, then energy will be released, and the amount of that energy will be according to the strength of the bond.

This seldom happens in the ordinary course of nature, for stability has been established in the compounds, as we have seen. It does happen occasionally as when lightning, for instance, causes wood to 'catch fire' as the strange phrase goes. Actually it does not catch anything, it is transformed into fire on account of the extraneous force snapping the bonds and accelerating the motion of the atoms of oxygen to form the new compound of carbon dioxide. This transmutation, this electrical reaction, is known as a chemical reaction, and it is upon such liberations of energy that the whole of modern civilization is built up. In our search for power we have been able to use the slow reaction from the unstable compound of coal, and get heat to change water into steam that will push a piston and drive an engine; or we can release energy in a vaporized combination so quickly in a series of combustions that we can dispense with the intermediary of water and steam; or we can release energy in a mixture of sulphur, charcoal, and saltpetre so very much more quickly that it will burst its container in an explosion. But the compounds of the world are nearly all stable. We cannot easily loose the bonds of the minerals, we cannot burn stones or metals. By a lucky chance we can liberate the energy and thus destroy by transmutation the substance of coal which is squashed primeval forest, which on account of certain geological conditions did not slowly burn (or rot) into carbon dioxide; and we can liberate the energy in oil which by another lucky chance is squashed marine organisms.

It was clear that the chemical sources of energy were limited, and that we might soon be compelled to return again to the unlimited supplies of wind and water. Then, at the turn of this century, we discovered the *inner* bonds of the atom. Before the discovery of radioactivity the play of the outer electrons had been recognized sufficiently to promote the application of chemistry; but it was not known that another atom, as it were, existed within the atom itself—the final nucleus. The famous 'splitting' of the atom really means opening the inner sanctuary of the nucleus. The radioactive elements showed that it was sometimes splitting open on its own account and at its own pace, and incidentally causing the transmutation of the element involved. I say 'incidentally', though there was a time when the possible transmutation of elements was a wonderful dream. The alchemists of old clung to the idea that such a thing was possible, and in their primitive laboratories strove to turn base metal into gold. We can do this today: at least theoretically we can, but we do not want to, and might just as well turn gold into base metal, since any element from which we can release nuclear energy is worth many times its weight in gold—for while a gramme of gold is worth about seven shillings, a gramme of lithium is worth about three thousand pounds.

That pound's worth of power can be got out of a gramme of lithium. We have noted how the amount of energy released in a chemical reaction corresponds to the strength of the bonds. But the binding of the outer electrons is nothing compared with the strength of the inner nuclear knots. The question was how to untie them, for it was one thing to break a molecule and get a chemical reaction, but quite another to break a nucleus and get an alchemical reaction. Even Rutherford thought it could not be done. 'It is like trying to shoot a gnat in the Albert Hall in pitch darkness,' he said to Mr. Ritchie Calder, 'and using ten million rounds on the off-chance of hitting it.' But, as we know, Sir John Cockcroft was not of that opinion, and other methods have now been devised by means of which the nuclei are encouraged to shoot at each other in a kind of furnace called a cyclotron.

At first we may feel surprised that so much power should reside in this minute place—any power at all, let alone more than that of ten million tigers. We are surprised because we have been slow to learn what energy actually *is*. We must remember that the nucleus is the only part of the earth where matter really exists—all else that we see is façade and fable, all else is pretence, posturing, hollowness, sham. Here only is true concentration, here only the clenched embrace of matter when it can truly be called mass. And what is mass? Einstein came forward and said $E = M$. A great saying: one of those supreme utterances when the revolutions of nations are already decided and histories unwritten are written. Energy equals Mass. Mass is Energy made manifest in concrete form. Energy is not indestructible. Matter is not indestructible. One can be converted into the other like work and heat. We do not need a lot of mass (or what we in our ignorance think of as mass) to get a lot of energy. The loss of mass which will give us an alarming amount of power cannot be discerned by the naked eye. Given the equation and the high mathematical knowledge required; given the equation, more strictly stated as $E = mc^2$ (meaning that the loss of mass must be multiplied by the square of the velocity of light), then it is possible to calculate a fixed scale of convertibility. We can calculate that an alchemical reaction is ten million times greater than a chemical reaction in terms of combustion. We can calculate that one gramme of uranium harbours energy equal to nineteen tons of T.N.T., and that it will give a million horse-power for thirty-three hours—which is what America and Canada jointly draw from Niagara in that time. We can calculate that one tenth of an ounce of radium will give out the energy of a ton of coal. We can calculate that since one pound of coal burned at Battersea Power Station keeps one electric fire going in one household for four hours, then the same lump of coal if converted into direct energy would keep all the electric fires in all the households in the United Kingdom going day and night for a month. Consider the omnipresence of this power. It lies hidden in the fortress of all the nuclei of all the atoms; it lies sleeping within every thing, within every stone, within every piece of bread and lump of cheese, within ourselves!

Our immediate task is over. Our goal is reached. We open the furthest door and behold the last links of the mighty locks. Here, in this unlikely place, we come upon the throne of majesty; here, concealed from mortal sight, dungeoned from the light of day, wholly lacking in all the props and appointments of power, in these forever exiled halls—the final, awful essence sits in state. It was not surprising that there was some heart-searching about this at first. 'Canst thou bind the sweet influences of Pleiades, or loose the bands of Orion?' asked God of Job when rehearsing the grandeur of His conception and the amplitude of His arm. Should we loose the bonds that hold the earth together, thus unstabilizing the stability? We have wondered about this. And it shall be written of our day, that having unfolded and still unfolded the mystery of matter until he came to stand before the last stronghold, Man paused. He hesitated. Should he take this citadel? Should he enter in at this gate? When at length, in August 1945, it became possible for him to use the knowledge, he said—*No: we should not have come to this place.* And so thinking, he turned and loosed these powers against himself.

vi

THE SUN

Still, Hiroshima may prove to be the pea-shooter's return. At least there are real signs that mankind is afraid of nuclear

21

war and may now stop. I live on that assumption myself. I am more encouraged to do so since the arrival of Zeta means that the physicists have not only given us a good reason for not waging war, but have taken away the main object of conquest—material gain in terms of gold or coal or oil or slaves. Uranium is a scarce commodity; but if in future we can get all the power we want by dipping a cup into the sea we need never go to war to plunder that. And I am not prepared to argue on rational grounds that we should not interfere with the nucleus, since there is no more *reason* why we should refrain from snapping the inner bonds to give us an alchemical reaction than from the now time-honoured practice of snapping the outer bonds to give us the ordinary chemical reaction.

What immediately concerns us in this study is the fact that atoms are the source of light. 'Every kind of light has its beginnings in atoms.'[1] We think of light as primarily coming from the sun. But sunlight also comes from the earth—or can be made to do so. For the earth is a bit of the sun which has 'gone out'. The sun consists largely of the same materials as the earth in a chain-reaction of transmutation. It is therefore not surprising that we can turn pieces of the earth into sun again. An atomic pile can do this. The sun is a glorified atomic pile.

I must expand this last statement. During some hundreds of years the chief question concerning the sun which exercised the minds of the scientists was: How does the sun keep alight? The earth was a piece of the sun thrown into space. It cooled. Why does the sun not cool? What keeps it going?

As is usual in the history of science many ingenious, imaginative, plausible, and even amusing theories were

[1] E. N. da C. Andrade: *The Atom and Its Energy.*

advanced in answer to this. Thus they said at first that it was
simply a gigantic fire getting its energy by combustion like
a burning pile of coal. Then they calculated that if this were
so, and even if it were burning best-quality Newcastle Coal,
it would peter out after five thousand years. (I would have
said five months.) They added that if it were using coal as
fuel the heat would be only one millionth part of the energy
actually emitted. After this Hermann von Helmholtz came
forward with his gravitational contraction theory which
amounted to the idea that the terrific pull of gravitation
would cause such a falling inwards as to generate energy,
and that this would account for sunshine already having
lasted for two thousand million years. But since this would
mean a shrinkage of the sun's radius amounting to 0·0003
per cent every century, it was realized that such rapidity
ruled the theory quite out of court. This was followed by
what may fairly be called the Perpetual Accident idea, which
was that the sun did receive fuel from outside itself and was
in fact being steadily stoked up by the fall of meteors upon
its surface. In order to maintain a balance between income
and expenditure the accretion would have to be about
equal to the loss in radiation. In view of the fact that such
addition should be roughly four million tons every second,
the theory was soon dropped.

Happily, speculation is now at an end and there is agree-
ment as to the solution of this problem. It is now understood that the sun is not on fire: that the sun is not burning.
It is hot; but it is too hot to burn. We cannot strictly use
the word burn in this connexion, nor speak of chemical
combustion. Its energy is recruited by the transformation
of hydrogen into helium. There was a time when seeing a
picture of some huge atomic pile I wondered vaguely why
in order to split so minute an object as an atom you need a

building about the size of Westminster Abbey. The reason is that the only way to smash atoms on a big scale is to get them to smash one another. This can be done if a sufficient heat is generated within a confined space to make them move fast enough. That is the general principle of the atomic plant. The sun is an atomic plant on rather a large scale. In early days, I am told, Jeans once expressed doubt to Eddington as to whether the sun were really hot enough for this. 'Well, go and find a hotter place!' said Eddington.

It is a cosmic furnace which possesses, as a furnace should, a rim. This is called its gas wall, quite as effective as any wall we could think of, which is held in place by the gravitational pull. How did it come to acquire the sufficient million degrees of heat to promote thermonuclear reactions? Again by the gravitational force. The sun started as a comparatively cool volume of gas which gradually became hotter and hotter on account of progressive gravitational contractions which cause great release of energy. When it became so hot that nuclear reactions took place then those same reactions stopped further contraction and a stable sun was the result.

The heat is so great and thus the atomic movement so swift that the outer electrons are stripped off and no atomic 'flesh' impedes the clash of the naked nuclei. Walt Whitman spoke of 'the splendid silent sun'. I have often wondered whether up there it is really silent. Should there not be a series of terrible explosions? This would certainly be so if the material were not just right, so to speak. It is known that hydrogen is the main stuff of the universe, but if there were much lithium as well, then the reaction through lithium into helium would take place in a matter of seconds and the sun would be shattered into bits. If there were much oxygen it would be too slow. George Gamow relates how the great scientist, Hans Bethe, worked the thing out: ' "It should not be so difficult after all to find the reaction which would just fit our old sun," thought Dr. Hans Bethe, returning home by train to Cornell from the Washington Conference on Theoretical Physics of 1938, at which he first learned about the importance of nuclear reactions for the production of solar energy; "I must surely be able to figure it out before dinner!" And taking out a piece of paper, he began to cover it with rows of formulas and numerals, no doubt to the great surprise of his fellow-passengers. One nuclear reaction after another he discarded from the list of possible candidates for the solar life supply; and as the Sun, all unaware of the trouble it was causing, began to sink slowly under the horizon, the problem was still unsolved. But Hans Bethe is not the man to miss a good meal simply because of some difficulties with the Sun, and redoubling his efforts he had the correct answer at the very moment when the passing dining-car steward announced the first call for dinner. Simultaneously with Bethe, the same thermonuclear process for the Sun was proposed in Germany by Dr. Carl von Weizsacher, who was also the first to recognize the importance of cyclic nuclear reactions for the problems of solar energy production.'[1]

What it all amounts to is that hydrogen is transformed into helium, not directly but through a cyclic sequence in which carbon and nitrogen play the part of catalysts. A catalyst is a formidable word meaning nurse. Carbon and nitrogen nurse hydrogen into helium, and just as nurses in a hospital, surrounded by dying patients and maternity wards, are themselves fresh and often in high spirits, so carbon and nitrogen take no harm from the reaction at which

[1] *The Birth and Death of the Sun.*

they assist. The final result of this chain reaction—a circular movement—is the formation of one helium nucleus; and one gramme of hydrogen transformed into helium will liberate an amount of energy which may be described in heat units as 166 thousand million calories, or in work units as 200 thousand kilowatt hours. The radiation of the sun is maintained by this exchange occurring millions of millions of times a second.

Is then the sun losing bulk? Yes indeed. Radiation carries mass with it. Since a ray of light makes an impact, a strong enough light directed on a man could knock him down as if with a jet of water. Any body emitting radiation is losing bulk—or weight. The sun is losing four million tons a second, or 250 million tons a minute—which, Jeans suggests, is 650 times the rate at which water is streaming over Niagara. He goes on to say that, 'If it has radiated at this rate for the whole three thousand million years or so since the earth came into existence, its total loss of mass would be 400,000 million million million tons.' When I first read those words I felt nervous. All that gone already, and four million tons going every second! Thinking how much one ton of coal makes, it didn't seem to me that we could have the sun with us much longer. But then Jeans adds that even so the loss of those 400,000 million million million tons represents only one part in five thousand of its total mass; and that we may say that each square inch of the sun's surface is only losing about a twentieth of an ounce a century. At this I plucked up spirits again.

Even so, if the sun does keep going for about ten billion years, should it not get cooler? No, it seems that it will get hotter before its final period. This should not surprise us. We do not expect our ordinary coal fires to become less hot as the fuel in the grate is consumed. We know that it frequently gets hotter, while if it is fed too unscientifically by a woman (for women do not understand fires) it will be much cooler for some time. The analogous mechanism of the sun is the changing opacity in the body of the gas while helium is built up. But enough of this. Let us come to Light.

CHAPTER TWO

The Nature of Light

i

WHAT IS LIGHT?

THE nature of light is by no means immediately obvious. If, in complete ignorance, we were to consider it during the day we might well think that it is a thing filling space—rather like air. Then, if during that day we were to go into a room and pull down dark blinds over the windows we would be surprised to find that the room no longer contained any of this thing. It was in the room when we pulled down the blinds and it has not escaped through any hole, but it is no longer present as the air is. Therefore it must be something which is continually arriving, and having arrived it must be instantly absorbed or scattered.

We learn the general statement—that light joins us from the sun after travelling ninety-three million miles in eight minutes. Even so it is not a strictly accurate statement. Light does not exist on its own. It is inaccurate to say that it comes to us in the sense that it is inaccurate to say that a pain has been thrown at me by a boy who has hit me in the face with a stone. The pain is the *result* of the stone travelling through the air and hitting me. If it had not hit me but had broken a window the result would have been different. All I can say is that a force has hit me and has had a certain effect upon me. The sun sends out force, not light or heat. Neither light nor heat has any existence on its own any more than there can be a smell of onions without an onion. The force exists on its own, but it is the results of force which we observe and experience. Various rays go out from the sun, and some of them when they strike an object cause light to scatter and heat to be felt. They must meet the object before light can be seen or heat felt. At night we gaze up into the sky. It is all dark. But beyond the confines of the earth's shadow it should not be dark, it should not be cold; it should be streaming with sunshine, it should be boiling hot—*if* light and heat existed on their own. We can prove this by going up there and being burnt to death in a blaze of sunshine. We need not do so since we have the moon to do it for us. There it hangs, that famous lamp—though itself a barren lightless rock.

Yet sunshine is not all of one piece. It is composed of a considerable number of different rays or waves each of which perform a particular function when they strike the earth. One wave is interpreted by our minds through the instrument of the eye as light. One is experienced as heat. Another, not the heat-ray, makes us sunburnt. And so on. Each possesses distinctive properties of frequency and length—though by length we do not mean the length of wave but of crest-distance from the preceding one. The frequency of their arrival is thus in accordance with their length just as the frequency of Atlantic rollers arriving on the west coast of Ireland is less than that of ripples on a pond in Surrey.

I need not stress that the waves which make it possible for us to experience luminosity and heat seem to be the most precious—but others exist equally vital. Just as heat-waves are incompetent to excite vision so also there are waves, which though feeble as regards heat and powerless as regards light, are yet of the highest importance on account of their capacity to produce chemical action. In fact they feed us. The whole vegetable world may be considered as a vast Mill receiving its motor-power from the sun. This is so much more than a mere figure of speech that some scientists speak of organic phenomena as altered or differentiated sunshine.

ii

THE MILLS OF GOD

A French cook who was preparing a mouth-watering meal was deeply pained when a friend of Henri Fabre claimed that he knew some one who could produce it all quite easily out of three bottles which he showed the cook. One bottle had nothing in it but air, the other only water, the third a bit of carbon. The cook considered himself a great artist, and he felt affronted by the suggestion that a still greater artist could produce the same wonderful meal out of the contents of those three bottles. Yet so it is. That supreme artist, the green vegetable cell, given a portion of hydrogen, nitrogen, oxygen, and carbon, can, through means of sunlight, build a bacillus, a tree, a mouse, or a man.

Above all, carbon. It seems that carbon is the main staff of life. If we take anything to bits we find that it possesses carbon. The way to take an organic thing to bits is to apply heat to it so that its more volatile particulars fly off. We all know what happens when we do this to bread or sugar or almost anything—we are left with a residue of carbon. So with plants, animals, or ourselves—we can all be reduced to carbon. It is odd that the stuff itself looks so inglorious,

for this black substance which smudges the coal-heaver and
the chimney-sweep is the insignia of all that is most colourful
on earth, responsible for the parade and panoply of
the living world no less than for the glittering of the
diamond.

We must have carbon. But neither ourselves nor the
animals can take it neat—a strong dose of it would poison
us. We cannot take it until it has been mixed with something else and is no longer in the form of gas but of concrete
substance. The plants on the other hand must take it neat.
That carbon is wafted about in the air above their heads.
But it is joined with oxygen. The plants do not want the
oxygen; yet the two are held together in a tight embrace.
They have been welded by the ordeal of fire. How then
unburn a stuff forged in the furnace? How pluck from
these aerial wanderers the material for the oak and the
grass?

Two things are needed: an agent capable of selection,
and a force at the service of the agent. The first of these is
supplied by that monarch among molecules belonging to
the pigment called chlorophyll; and the second by sunlight.

A leaf is riddled with thousands of tiny orifices or mouths
which we call stomata. These provide its breathing apparatus. Through these it takes in the same air as we do, though
what it wants, as we have seen, is not the oxygen but the
carbon. The solution enters and meets with a number of
little round bladders filled with a kind of paint, the leaf-
green, the chlorophyll. When the sunbeams meet these
molecules the work begins, the great work that enthrones
the vegetable cell as king, with men and wolves for subjects.
First, the beams play upon the leaf and set it tingling all
over. The green rays of light come back to our eyes, while

the others—chiefly the long wave-lengths—are absorbed into the interior. The chlorophyll molecule responds to them, takes up energy, and thus fortified turns out the oxygen and sets free the carbon. It undoes previous work, as it were, unburning the burnt and de-consuming the consumed. The carbon at once joins itself with the ascending sap to make sugar and starch. All this is done with the swift simplicity of natural miracle; several synthetic steps are taken in less than a second. Building blocks hewn from the primary elements are cast into the crucible, soon to be assembled as grass or tree.

We use a word for this—photosynthesis. And when we use this word 'photosynthesis' what are we saying? We are saying that here is dross; here are bits and pieces; here is matter, cold and lifeless, turned suddenly into living tissue. We are present on the Third Day. This is Genesis. That happened a long time ago we think: yet it happens still, it happens now before our eyes every moment that the beaming blows of light strike on the leaf. These are the mills of God. The solar flood beats on the blades, the flukes fly forward, and the green factory in which the living world is forged, is kept in motion. This is inexhaustible creation. The engine and its agent are wholly unconditioned. For that power is the great sun itself, far removed from earthly weal or woe, unharmed, untouched by any mishaps of the world. And the cholorophyll is largely omnipresent. Whatever man or mouse may choose to do or leave undone, these two agents of the Mover, from everlasting to everlasting, weave living substance from the lifeless air.

From the air. Thence come all things living. We are condensed and consolidated air. We are the offspring of the heavens and the children of light.

32

We forget this, and at first even doubt its truth as we look round. We see the plants rising from the soil. Are they not laid upon the lap of earth? Do they not lip their mother's milk from down below? They do indeed. They are breast-fed there. But only breast-fed—with mineral water. They must have water though they may sometimes do without soil, as we see in the rootless chlorella carpeting a pond, or when we make seeds grow upon a sponge. And plants can grow from watered soil in darkness; but they are then plant-ghosts and come to nothing, while if air is taken away they perish at once. For every mouth below a thousand mouths must feast above. The rose on the bush, the rose in the cheek cannot bloom without carbon any more than the diamond can shine—which is the purest form of carbon. It is wonderful to observe how plants will appear simply in answer to the presence of light, be it but a lamp. Go into a cave. Venture right into the underground world opened up by the spelæologists. This is the realm of darkness. Here little grows. Yet if the spelæologists have fixed lanterns here and there upon the walls of the tunnels, and have kept them continuously shining, green plants will grow around them. You can see them in Wookey Hole in Somerset; wherever there is a lamp, then growing in the crevices of the damp rock, we see a cluster of green vegetation. How did they get there? It is hard to say. Light had called them, and they came.

Thus what we see below in glowing forms of life came from above. Imagine the earth before organic life had come. On the one hand, rock: on the other, gas. A bare and grievous land below a poisoned sky fed by the convulsions of vulcanicity and the electric sparks from the storm-clouds. Yet in that angry sky above those hopeless rocks dwelt all that was to be made manifest below; from that tumult and disorder came the organs; from out that fearful riot in the raging flimsy air came all that blooms in plants and moves in creatures, all that smiles and weeps; from those foggy hosts of carboned gas came the vehicle for sensation, thought, conscience, and the word—nay, Plato too sat waiting there, and the body of Christ.

We go forward from that scene through the centuries till we come to the Carboniferous Forests. That was the era in the history of the earth when trees ruled the world. Their empire comprehended the greater part of all lands. The mind can scarcely seize it. Only the great oceans can compare in size with those forests. They rolled on from horizon to horizon—for once the first speck of protoplasm had been miraculously created the result grew to this, and the trees fed upon a sky saturated with carbonic acid gas many times thicker than it is today. Thus as yet there were no animals nor even insects. We rather shrink at the thought of such a scene; not bare like the desert, not hostile like the sea—but lifeless. We cannot imagine trees whose boughs were birdless, nor gladly think of long-drawn summer days unchoired by bees. Yet so it was. No animal could breathe that acid-poisoned air. It must first be cleansed: atmospheric purification was the primary work of trees. Toiling on through uncalendared centuries, without sound or movement in the speechless glades, they pastured on our poison.

In summary: the plants, whose unbloodied kingdom stretches across the whole world, alone of all living things flourish without hunting and feed without slaughter, simply turning the sky into the tissues of their temples. The sheep consumes grass, the man consumes mutton; neither has yet made any contribution as primary creators; such elaboration is confined to the soundless mills of the

green cell in combination with the inexhaustible floods of
light poured ceaselessly upon the earth. It is the vegetable
which creates the substances, it is the animal which consumes and destroys them. But now a circular movement
has been attained which is helpful to plants. The animals
permanently pass into the air the acids which the plants
need: what the one gives to the atmosphere the other takes.
Thus the Circle, thus the Wheel turns for ever at its task;
the vegetables perpetually decompose the carbonic acid,
fixing the carbon and setting free the oxygen, while the
animals take the food in the form prepared and perpetually
breathe out that gas: the plants, feasting upon the fumes of
putrefaction and turning the relics of death into meadows of
life, give us green pastures; so that even in our age, riddled
as it is with scientific terminology, we can still pay tribute
to the simplicity and grandeur of the theme with the rooted
ancient words—*All flesh is grass*.

iii

COLOURS

The radiations from the sun do more than light the earth
and feed it. They decorate it. Until Newton appeared it was
not known that all flowers are black. No one realized that
not one single colour belongs to any object intrinsically,
and that all objects are black or no-colour. This is contrary
to our common sense. We see the yellow daffodil growing
up out of the ground, and it seems clear that its colour, the
most emphatic thing about it, grows up with it, belongs to
it, is it. Yet no; that yellow on the daffodil, that red on the
rose was eight minutes ago in the sun.

Before this was discovered in the seventeenth century little was known as to the nature of light and no one had thought of attempting to split it up. It was left for the great Newton to appear with his prism in the dark room. Even today the little experiment still fascinates us. We go into a dark room; we make a neat hole in the blind; a ray of sunshine passes across the room to a screen. Then we place a prism (roughly a piece of glass with at least three sides) in the path of the ray. Instead of the beam passing on—though bent by the glass—we see separate bands of light each of a different colour, the most obvious being red, orange, yellow, green, blue, and violet. A beam of ordinary white light, any thread of it however thin, is a bundle of rays which can be fanned out by a prism because the particular wave-length or scale of each makes it subject to a particular degree of bending. Thus spread out each ray is discerned as a different colour. We close the fan and it is white again. We call this the Spectrum, the word simply meaning spectacle or appearance.

This is a few-centuries-old story now, but few of us are too sophisticated or too dull not to marvel at it. Of course there is no necessity to take a prism and go into a dark room in order to satisfy ourselves that colour exists in white light. We know that all we need is a garden, a garden-hose, and a sunny day. Then we turn on the hose, arranging the nozzle so that the water comes out as a fine spray, and stand with our backs to the sun—and there in front of us is a rainbow. The spray has done the work of the prism. It gives me satisfaction to conduct this small research in the only laboratory I possess, the open air. It is pleasant to be able to say—I can pluck colours from the empty air, and set them as an archway over the rose bushes.

Failing a garden and hose, we can simply use a spider's

web. When the sunshine is slanting at the end of the day I have often come upon the nets spreading out a good deal of the spectrum. A single dewdrop or raindrop hanging from a twig can be seen throwing back one colour and then another as we change our position. Failing these, we all have eyelashes and noses. They make as good equipment as any. If we sit down and turn our faces to the sun and then screw up our noses while half-closing the eyes (thus looking hideous to a spectator), we shall find that the very fine hairs on the bridge of the nose, together with our eyelashes, will stretch out most of the spectrum.

Thus, then, the waves of light fall upon the objects of the world. What happens depends upon the constitution of the object. One will absorb all the waves, and we get a black object; another will reject them all, and we get a white object; another will accept some and reject others, and we get a vari-coloured object. The black tulip has accepted all and gives us none; the white rose has accepted none and gives us all; the yellow daffodil has accepted most but gives us one. We might be inclined to suppose at first that the colours which the flower accepts should be colours we shall see. But it is a question of reflection. The yellow daffodil absorbs all the colour-rays except yellow which is sent back to our eyes. Thus when we look out upon the colours of the world we are not seeing those which are taken but those which are left. We must not think that the pure red rose in the garden has chosen that colour as its insignia, for red is the only colour which it has refused and cast away.

Can we satisfy ourselves visually that, though the spectrum exists, there are no colours on earth irrespective of it? Not by simple means, I think. I have sometimes read books, otherwise most enlightening, in which it is actually

said that if you take a flower into a dark room you find that
it has then no colour. But all we can tell in the dark is that
it is not luminous—which is an entirely different thing. Yet
if we are prepared to undertake extraordinary means there
is a way by which we can satisfy ourselves visually that no
colours exist in the objects on their own account. We can
do it if we pass steadily away from the light of the sun. If
instead of going up in a balloon into the heights of the air
we descend in a balloon into the depths of the sea we shall
behold objects changing their colour before our eyes as the
different waves of light grow weaker. Our companion of
course would be William Beebe who is accustomed to
journey into the deep dark realms of the ocean in his water-
balloon or bathysphere. Descending slowly one day, he
tells how when less than fifty feet beneath the surface he
happened to glance at a large prawn which he had taken
with him. Its colour is, as most people know, an attractive
scarlet. 'To my astonishment,' he relates, 'it was no longer
scarlet, but a deep velvety black.'[1] Subsequently he studied
the changing colours as he went down to fourteen thousand
feet. If we were to see this in quick-motion cinematography
we would have a picture of remarkable interest, and would
be visually convinced at once that these threads of light
are responsible for all the coloured patterns of the
world.

The ordinary absorption and rejection of waves is taken
into account by all of us in simple ways. Thus our chief
reason for playing tennis or cricket in whites is the knowledge that if we played in dark tints we would get too hot.
When Piccard took his famous gondola high into the air
he found it too hot with a dark covering and too cold with
a white one, and was at some pains to achieve a colour that

[1] *Adventuring with Beebe.*

would give him a comfortable temperature. Fortunes have sometimes been made on the turf by gamblers who have realized that on excessively hot days, other things being equal, a white horse has a better chance than a dark one. Mountain cottages which are whitewashed become far too cold and a dark colour is essential. At Hiroshima those who were dressed in white are said to have been spared the worst burns, while those wearing deep colours sustained the deepest injuries.[1]

The discovery of the spectrum made the analysis of spectra (called spectroscopy) possible in our own day. The composition of the rays gives information concerning the properties of the stars. Since matter and energy are the two sides of the same coin we can learn the nature of the matter by the composition of the energy. We are cut off from the material body of the stars by the barrier of impenetrable space. But though the stars conserve their matter they cast abroad their energy. The very barrier of space is no barrier, for it is massed with messages. If we study the radiations we can learn what sort of atoms emit them. They are the messengers who tell us what is going on millions of miles away. We study their story as if we were reading in a book. Swift in passage they are slow in arriving. Energy leaks from matter and streams through space at 186,000 miles a second. Even so the messengers from the Milky Way which went forth at the childhood of mankind have hardly yet arrived.

The scholars who translate these books of light are the geophysicists.[2] Others deal with the visible, they deal with

[1] See L. Cheskin: *Colour: What It Does for Us.*
[2] I content myself with merely defining this remarkable science. See Herbert Dingle's brilliant *Modern Astrophysics*, and for easy terms see J. H. Fabre's *The Heavens.*

the invisible. Others are at home with the things of earth, they are at home with the things of space. They analyse the colour quality of the radiation. It teaches them of what materials, of what molten metals, the sun consists—its iron, its copper, its zinc. Thus from a study of light we learn about the source of light and discover that largely the same bricks have been laid to the foundation of the heavens as of the earth.

iv

THE WONDERLAND

We can see what the world would look like if the accepted colours were apparent to us. Indeed one of the most interesting ways of making the mystery of light-and-colour real to ourselves is by simply putting a prism to our eyes. Then we come upon it with a flash of surprise. Yet it is noteworthy that not a few of those who know all about the prism and the spectrum (in the famous school way of knowing things) do not know what happens if they simply put a prism to their eyes—and probably they think that they do not possess one. But any piece of smooth glass with three sides will do. Personally I use one of the glass fingers which used to hang from a lampshade.

We look through it and see a very different world. So fantastic is the change that at first we may suspect some trickery in the glass. I looked at a line of washing, chiefly white. Through the glass the things appeared rainbowed. The white towel hanging there had a band of orange at the top with parallel bands below of red, green, yellow, blue, and violet. I turned my attention to an area of earth on which I had made a bonfire, consisting now of odd bits and pieces of sticks, silver paper, burnt heads of tins and so forth, on the edge of which was a flower-pot in a white saucer. Through the glass all was transfigured. The flower-pot stood in a bright rainbow. The tawdry piece of tin became a pearl of great price. The sticks and flints and ridges of clay and ash were coloured walls surrounding something like the Tower of London done up as a fairy palace. A seagull, happening to alight there just then, became nearly a peacock in colour-scheme. A well-to-do thrush whose frontage faced the sunlight achieved a fancy-waist-coat.

I took away the prism from my eyes and saw again the bleak area of rubbish. Yet there was nothing in the glass by way of colour to make this transformation.

I looked again. The twigs of a bush which had no leaves on it were dripping with rainbow. A pear-tree with young leaves fully catching the sunlight became a Christmas Tree all lit up with candles, some upright and others upside-down. In this case the 'wax' in many colours gave the light. A breeze shook the tree and all the candles waved about without danger of falling off; and so long as the sun shone the candles would burn and the wax not waste. I would use the same image for that flower-pot in the white saucer on the rubbish heap: it was standing in a fire of coloured flames.

I then looked at some withered dandelions. They had come to life again, as also had the withered head of a daffodil: for in this new land there is no death nor sad last days, nor ruin and degradation. A bit of white rag had been thrown upon the path: when I caught sight of it through the glass I wondered what I was looking at—for no flower could shine more bright. A smudge upon the window from inside a greenhouse looked like the Crown Jewels.

Looking up at the houses in this way I saw that all the rims of all the roofs were blue and violet—most lovely and most strange. The white-walled houses threw back all the spectrum, glittering through the trees; and every window which caught the sun aslant was blazed likewise with the bands. So as not to over-multiply impressions I will merely note further that in this mode the gravel path became a Persian carpet, that the hanging pieces of tin-foil which my neighbour had put up to scare the birds looked like strangely coloured fish leaping about, and that a page of my writing became an illuminated manuscript.

The paradox about thus seeing the true colours as received on earth is that they give the impression of not belonging to the objects at all, whereas the colours which really do not belong appear to be absolutely integrated. Those blue-rimmed roofs of the houses look as if they had been superimposed by some artist with singular ideas. Another thing is that the objects are not so clearly defined, they are misted and fogged, their fringes blurred. That white shirt upon the line becomes a shirt-ghost, the violet at its lower end being almost translucent. Things which are particularly hard look soft and insubstantial. I was astonished to see that my garden spade was composed of rainbowed fog, and that my clippers lying on the ground reflecting the sun were made of coloured mist—tools fit for heavenly use maybe, but on earth, what dig with this, what cut with those?

Again I look at the glass: it has nothing in it with which to make these changes—save the power to separate the rays. These colours reveal the reality of the waves that paint the rose and gild the lily.

The earth seen in this way is not often as beautiful as when we see it straight. It is sometimes astonishing, as when the wretched rag which has been cast aside is embroidered with bright colours, or the tawdry tin is crowned with jewels; but often it seems a gaudy world and lacking in definition. Purity of line and form have vanished. The rose is ruined; the moon is bilious; the glorious whiteness of the cloud is turned to sickly sunset. We would not care to dwell in this prismed world; but by looking through the glass we get a partial glimpse of the intricate paths and winding ways of light.

v

SKY COLOURS

Though the mystery of colour was solved three centuries ago, the reason why there is such constant light around us and why the sky is blue has only been really decided more recently. If the force of light must wait till it strikes something before appearing as luminosity, how are we able to see the sky flooded with light? Should it not be dark save for what it receives by way of reflected light from the earth?—so that on the plain the light above us would be very poor, while in the mountains the crags would shine like the moon. The answer is that the so-called empty air is packed with objects massed in sufficient millions to give us the flood-lit sky. Nowadays we are in no danger of imagining that the invisible is necessarily immaterial. The whole of modern physics is based on the fact, as we have seen, that atoms and molecules while less easy to discern than whales are just as physical.

Of course there is a great deal of fine dust in the air up to five thousand feet. It plays some part in scattering the waves of light. It is generally invisible, yet we have all seen it from time to time in the country when the sky is bright but also blocked with weighty clouds sometimes offering just a small hole through which the sun can pass. This familiar spectacle is always delightful and even symbolic. For then a clear beam pierces the gloom like a reversed searchlight or like the shaft above the audience in a cinema, fixing one place for our attention. I have hung a few such pictures in the academy of my memory. One day while working on a high field in Dorset in a close and thundery atmosphere, a hole in one dark cloud let a sun-shaft through. It slanted down to earth, a white beam caused by the thousand million dust-flakes as reflectors, and rested upon a derelict stable in the vale below. It stayed there fixedly. All else was gathered in the pensive gloom, but the beaming finger continued to point to this one ruined and most wretched place as to some truth or treasure.

Nevertheless the invisible dust has only a limited effect on the total illumination of the sky, or with the fact that it is seen as blue. It was thought for some time that the particles of water-vapour were responsible. So Tyndall thought, but it was later established by Lord Raleagh that the chief agents are the molecules of the air itself. 'The air molecules', says Bragg, 'are of course very small, much smaller than the wave-length of light, but the cumulative action of a vast number of minute amounts of scattering of the separate molecules is enough to account for the light that we receive from the blue sky.'[1]

The reason why the sky is seen as blue is to be explained by molecule-power in intercepting wave-lengths of light.

[1] *The Universe of Light.*

The molecules sift them out. Some of the waves, being shorter than others, are easier to filter. It seems that the air molecules are the right size to intercept the blue waves and scatter them abroad so that we get an impression of blue. When we look at the far-away hills they appear to be blue, and we build hopes on them, and our hearts are raised. But as we approach they lose their glamour and the crags turn grey and comfortless, for they have not been clothed in their own right but are subject to the fleeting falsities of the air. It is not so easy for the molecules to scatter the larger waves just as it is not so easy for a rock in the sea to scatter a large wave as a short one. The short waves that compose the blue portion of the spectrum are more easily turned aside than the red waves, but as evening comes on the sun lies low on the horizon and its rays are obliged to traverse many more miles of atmosphere and much more dust than at noon. Most of the shorter waves are filtered out—rather in the same way as when we go down in the bathysphere with Beebe—while the longer ones, the orange, the ruby, and the rose give us the celebrated colours of the sunset.

This is not to say that we cannot on occasion have a green sun or a blue moon. Both have been seen, but not often. More than one observer, including M. Minnaert, have perceived a bright green sun when an engine emitting clouds of steam has temporarily obscured the orb. In fact M. Minnaert got a blue sun as well as a green one out of this.[1] Such phenomena have been witnessed lasting for hours, and without benefit of steam-engines; while after the famous eruption of Krakatoa when vast quantities of fine volcanic dust were hurled into the highest layers of the atmosphere and did not settle down literally for years,

[1] See his *Light and Colour in the Open Air.*

people were able to behold far and wide in the world, not only green and blue moons, but sunsets and sunrises of unexampled splendour.

It is possible to see coloured clouds at high noon; but these are more properly called iridescent clouds and they belong to the same family, as it were, as the halo, the corona, the aureole, the fog-bow, the dew-bow, and other rings all caused by complicated diffraction of light by drops of water and mist, some exhibiting pleasant effects as when the shadowed head of saint or sinner is crowned with glory. The term *Heilgenschein* is reserved for the remarkable aureole of light just above the shadow of our heads when in the early morning we stand on the dewy grass with our backs to the slanting sun. A special light gathers round our own heads no matter where we move, though we can discern nothing of the kind surrounding the shadowed heads of our companions on the lawn—a pleasing phenomenon which led Benvenuto Cellini to conclude that the shimmer was the insignia of his genius.

It would seem natural to suppose that the aurorae belong to the same category as coronae and haloes, the most famous being the Aurora Borealis seen at high altitudes in the northern and southern skies, looking like an illuminated supernatural aeroplane. But these effects are said to derive from disturbances on the sun and to be associated with the solar prominences and spots when colossal jets of protons and electrons are sprayed out toward the earth at three thousand miles a second, and eventually hit the atoms and molecules of the upper air, electrifying them and making them glow as ghostly streamers of coloured light or as veils and curtains that have caught fire from some cosmic catastrophe.

vi

THE RAINBOW

Let us get back to the ordinary—which generally turns out to be just as extraordinary as the extraordinary. We have already noted how the rainbow exhibits the spectrum. Yet why should we get an arch? The answer is that we do not: we get part of a circle—the whole of which we can discern from a very high place. Again, why only this one circle? Once more we are mistaken: there are many, though we can see only one or two of them. Even so it is surprising. Granted that the water-drops act as prisms fanning out the waves of light, why do we not see a chaos of colours, a ragged and incoherent conglomeration on the screen? How comes it that we see the neat perfect circle? By what means does a shower of water meeting a shaft of light achieve such form? On what spindle and by what potter are the wheels whorled?

It is done by virtue of those geometrical laws which are our comfort and our stay. If our hearts leap up at the sight of a rainbow in the sky, it is made possible by geometry, that mystery lying at the foundations of Nature, as if it were the first of the tools of God. Thus we are told, as a sort of Rule One of the business, that the angle of refraction is exactly equal to the angle of incidence—as it falls so it bends away. It might *not* have been thus ordered. We might have supposed that it could be inconsistent in its behaviour like a refractory child. But never. This is comforting. And it makes for beauty.

Still, how comes it that we get our circle? Imagine a rain-drop the size of a plum. It acts as a detainer for some rays, though others pass straight through it. Those which strike its top and bottom are bent inwards and go to the farther edge of the drop which acts as the wall of a mirror, so that the ray comes back to our eyes. Multiply this process so that it is acting all round the drop; and multiply the drop by myriads, though each is being replaced by another as the rain falls!—and we get an inkling of what happens. Only an inkling, I admit. In seeking to avoid the execrable language of the specialists, which, believe me, frequently fails to convey sense, I am not likely to suggest more than a quarter of the operation, so seemingly complicated and yet with all of Nature's majestic simplicity—though I would prefer to make it appear too simple than too complex. And let us not lose sight of the truth about the rainbow which makes us interested in it in the first place—its beauty. In obedience to these marvellous geometrical laws the arches are set up to the delight of all mankind. Their appeal is greatest in the mountain regions, perhaps especially in that part of the world where the light that never shone on land or sea shines on sea and land—in Ireland. The rainbows that I saw in my youth hang before me still. As I write, I think of one. I had been wandering alone in the Wicklow Mountains during many hours of unbroken rain. The leaden sky looked down upon the level bog and the mountains were nothing worth. As late afternoon came on there was a break in the western sky, the sun came out, and the curtain in the east was lifted to reveal the hills from stony crag to curving lawn. It was still showering over there, and a great archway was set up, one pedestal on each side of a valley. At the foot of one, in the rainbow, I saw illuminated a shepherd boy waving his arms rather as if conducting an orchestra, evidently in communication with his dog, and on the other side I could see some transfigured sheep. A simple theme; a pastoral of old time; not quite departed from us yet—though less familiar than when Wordsworth wrote, 'Shout round me, let me hear thy shouts, thou happy shepherd boy!'

vii

FIRE

One of the main light-spectacles is when the heat-rays produce fire and we get light that way. We have the bundle of rays contained in the spectrum. Some of these rays do not disclose themselves visibly. Thus the ultra-violet waves which are beyond the visible violet ones make us sunburnt. At the other end beyond the red, are the invisible infra-red rays which produce heat. When they are strong enough they become visible in terms of flame—and that flame will itself give us the colours of the spectrum: it will give us the secondary sunshine which we call fire.

I have never found it easy to grasp what fire and flame really are, but I am unwilling to take them for granted. We all strike matches and light lamps and torches without giving a thought to the mystery of it, and regard those who do think about it as special people—'scientists'. It does seem to me worth while trying to break down this attitude.

Let us take heat first, and note that while it is proper to speak of heat as existing, it is not proper to speak of cold as existing *per se*. There is no such thing as cold save at 273° below. At that point it would be fair to say: Here is coldness. Otherwise it is a question of much or little heat. Sitting in a room I begin to 'feel chilly'. My body is a heat-container, the temperature being about 98°. If my clothes are not 'warm enough', that is if they fail to keep my heat *in*, then I will be letting some of it out into the less warm atmosphere of the room. So I get into bed. Provided I have some good blankets I will now be able to keep the heat in. I can demonstrate the fact that I am not keeping the cold out but the heat in by substituting a block of ice for myself in the bed. The blankets will not warm it up and make it melt: they will help to preserve it from melting. The air in the room though 'cold' is a good deal warmer than the ice, so if we put the block under blankets we can prevent that warmth from acting upon it. If we realize that there is no such thing as cold in its own right, we are all likely to be more sensible about clothes (as women are); for certain fabrics which are quite light keep in the heat better than heavy ones which simply make us tired. Probably paper clothes would be best from this point of view. Many a down-and-out man has found that a covering of newspaper at night keeps in the heat better than a blanket.

What is heat itself? It is the result of molecular movement—the temperature being in proportion to the rate at which the molecules are moving. When an object is struck by the rays of the sun its molecules are made to move faster, and it becomes hot. Fair enough. But why should fast-moving molecules give us this sensation of heat? I think that the answer is that we then *feel* the molecules, we feel their vibration. When the molecules of the air are made to move fast they are felt by our nerves and we call the sensation warmth. It is often a pleasant sensation. But if we thrust a hand into a very fast-moving bunch of molecules we draw it back quickly as if we had been bitten. We have been bitten—by the molecules. A burn is a bite, as it were: to be scorched is to be mauled by the molecules. But what is this *flame* which we see?

Take an unlit candle. There is a stick of wax: there is a thread of wick. That is all we see at first. Around it there is air which we do not see, nor any part of it—as yet. The molecules that compose the wax are moving at a certain rate but not fast enough to cause the solid to become a liquid. When, by the application of heat, they are made to go much faster the surface of the wax does become liquid and by the law of capillarity rises up through the wick. And then it is that from that wick which stands in the pool we see that an extra thing is now fastened—a little spear not made of metal, not made of liquid, not made of vapour, not made of cloth though it is like a little flapping flag, and if you pass your finger through it quickly it seems to have as much substance as the wind. Why should the hot wax take this form? Let us see. Invisible vapour rises from the wax-pool. Vapour is composed of molecules. Molecules are composed of atoms. Atoms possess their outer electrons. The atoms, on account of the speed at which they are now moving become vulnerable; they may lose their outer electrons and combine with other atoms to form a new thing. They combine with the atoms of oxygen in the air. The combination is attended by an explosion—though silent—and we get a spark, a multitude of sparks which make a flame. That flame, once it gets going, once that chemical reaction, as we say, has taken place, carries on by process of feeding upon the wax and feeding upon the oxygen. But we do not know why this action produces this form which we know as flame any more than we know why the combination of hydrogen and oxygen produces water. All we know is that when atoms emit energy, whether from the sun or the earth, we get light. We can describe Nature but we cannot explain the nature of Nature. I have kept a candle burning in front of my manuscript as I wrote these lines, and the more I gaze at the flame the less I suppose myself to understand the miracle of combination and the mystery of combustion with its translation of matter into the comfort of heat and the glory of light.

We do not always need a lighted match, a flame, to achieve a flame. Water will serve. But not in any way that is useful to us. Thus we build a large hayrick. Unfortunately we have made an error; we have carried the hay when it was too green and therefore contained a good deal of moisture. Without realizing this we go away and attend to other things. Later on we find that the hayrick has disappeared: it has changed into something else and gone off the field—in the form of fire. No match has been applied to it to set off the ordinary chain-reaction. No specially hot sun has been focused upon it. Nevertheless the molecules have been made to move very fast indeed. The moisture has been compressed and cannot escape in the form of gas, and the confined molecules strike against each other so violently that after a while there has occurred a sudden combination and a transformation into flame—for there was enough oxygen penetrating the interstices of the hay to make this possible.

Modern civilization is built on the efficient control of combustion in all its forms. On the occasions when we fail to control it fire changes from our comfort to our terrible enemy. Thus whole cities have been converted into this useless form and gone off, and we think of the great fire of Rome in A.D. 64 when two-thirds of the city went; of Venice in 1106 when nearly all the town passed; of Oslo in 1624 which had to be replaced by Christiana; of the Great Fire of London in 1666 when the greater part of the city was converted; of Moscow in 1812 thus leading to Napoleon's retreat; of the Houses of Parliament in 1834 and the Royal Exchange in 1838 being totally transmuted; of Chicago in

1871 when Mrs. O'Leary's cow kicked over a lantern and transformed a city; and so on, including the West Indian Dock fire of London in 1933 which also caused the river to become chiefly liquid rubber as witnessed by myself who swam out into it opposite Wapping, only to land as evidently a native of darkest Africa.

CHAPTER THREE

Reflections and Illusions

i

REFLECTIONS

LIGHT falls upon a tree. Some of the rays immediately bounce off and come to us so that we say—There is a tree. But they may also fall upon an object in front of us which we do not see at all. Instead we see—*ourselves*. The object is made of glass. We do not see the glass and are confronted with our own faces. We are now so accustomed to 'look in the mirror' that we take it for granted along with so much else. A mirror has always been regarded by primitive people as one of the most delightful gifts that we can give them. After the first shock of being confronted with themselves they have been quick to realize that if the glass is held at a given angle they can see things behind them; and some chiefs have made cunning use of thus being armed with eyes in the backs of their heads.

Nevertheless perhaps I may say in passing if it does not seem too frivolous that most of us still do get a shock when we try on a new suit in a tailor's shop in front of the series of mirrors which show us to ourselves as we appear from behind and side-faced. That frightful, sharp beak of a nose which we then behold is hard to contemplate with equanimity—if that is what we present to our friends. But I believe not. There is distortion I am happy to say. Looking from the top of a bus one day while going through a not very thrilling London street my dull gaze alighted upon a nice girl standing in a shop window. There was a mirror beside her reflecting her profile, which gave her a pen-sharp unpleasing nose not noticeable in the original. I felt quite cheered up. There is hope for us all.[1]

Why is it that we see ourselves instead of the glass? We do see it but it is obliterated by the picture of ourselves. The rays of light are scattered from the glass to us, and also from us to it. This happens all the time with everything but only smooth surfaces give a reflection—and scarcely any surfaces are strictly smooth. And they must be backed with quick-silver to prevent transmission. The ordinary window-pane will reproduce our image but only faintly. Sitting in the railway carriage in the evening the image is clear enough for us to be able to examine the face of the person in the corner without looking at him. We can watch him closely though he is not where we are looking—in fact passing trains run through him without hurting him. It is only the genuine mirror which gives us the image so clearly that we can see nothing else.

Yet to obtain an almost perfect mirror glass is not necessary. Water will do. In the ordinary way this is not quite true; but extraordinary effects can be obtained if the reflected objects are confined. The best example of what I mean is the reflection of the roof of the cave in the water below at Cheddar. The cave, of course, is not full of water, but at the side, pools have collected in hollows. As you walk along you see miniature lakes at the side of your path, the basins which contain them being on an elevation about level with your waist. The water (around which lights have been fixed) is wonderfully pure and still. As you gaze upon it you do not see the floor of the pool: you see the roof of the

[1] For mirrors and 'depth' see page 109.

cave directly above the water. You see it with remarkable clarity and particularity. Yet you see it not. That is not what you see. You see something quite different, far other than the roof of a cave! You see a hilly landscape with villages clumped here and there between the walled-in fields. It is as if you looked upon such a landscape from afar off and got a clear impression of brown fields and walls and villages and little churches. The illusion is extraordinary. You simply do not see a reflection of a dented ceiling upside-down. It is a mountain countryside which has been abandoned. All those fields are bare and all those streets are silent. No one comes from the village. No man enters the church. The melancholy of the scene thus set eternally in stone works upon us like a Grecian Urn:

> What little town by river or sea-shore,
>   Or mountain-built with peaceful citadel,
>   Is emptied of its folk, this pious morn?
> And, little town, thy streets for evermore
>   Will silent be; and not a soul to tell
>   Why thou art desolate, can e'er return.

Such effects of light and water are not ordinary. The ordinary ones are well known and well loved, for this subject touches us in so many ways and on so many levels. We all enjoy gazing at water which is chiefly sky, or chiefly trees and flowers. I have a pool in my garden. It was looking very dark yesterday in the late autumn afternoon, for though the sun was shining a fence and some shrubbery darkly shade it at this time of year. There is also a rowan-tree on one side. Its upper branches were well lit up—yellow enlightened with gold. I gazed upon the dark surface of the water, and as my eyes travelled down they travelled up into those branches, and so, while the surface of the water was gloomy, yet as I looked ever deeper things looked ever brighter—as if I were looking into a strange hole which instead of being light at the top and dark at the bottom was dark at the top and light at the bottom.

In another book I suggested that woods promote meditation in thoughtful men. I think that I am borne out in this by the experience of mankind. Yet perhaps still water in which the surrounding scene is reflected is even more conducive to serene contemplation. We speak of a man's *reflections*, implying something deeper than reasoning—thoughts arising from a mind which has been so stilled that the mud in it has sunk to the bottom and it can calmly reflect and give an untroubled image of reality. We love to sit alone by the quiet water in the evening light, not only because of the law by virtue of which things above are seen below so that when we are looking down into the water we are gazing up into the clouds, but because we enter into a serene and blessed mood and discern that reality is un-corrupted and purged of stain, and that this world of tragedy and dirge has suffered a transformation. We are calmed. We enter into harmony. We feel much as Chekhov felt when he listened to music and declared that all things are forgiven and that it would be strange not to forgive.

ii

THE BUBBLE

A bubble is a balloon. If we let out some air under water, what happens? Does it then mix with the water as vapour mixes with air? By no means. Its aim is to escape intact out of the element of water. But it does not fall upward through the water and join the air in the same way that a drop of water will fall downward through air. Drops of air do go upward at great speed—but they go as balloons whose covering is made of *water*. An ordinary balloon with gas in it lighter than air goes up swiftly into the sky. A water balloon with air in it goes up just as quickly. What is so remarkable is that the air should at once construct these spheres with lightning rapidity. It is doubtful whether any-one knows exactly how it is done. Anyway the doing of it should hold us all. For my part I find these small works of Nature as satisfactory and surprising as any of her major performances. I think that instead of gloomily 'waiting for Godot' we should have a look round at the world. If we did this we might cheer up a bit. For the fact is Godot is present—could we but see him. Paradise is here, said the mystic, Jacob Boehme, though man is not yet in paradise.

I mention the common bubble only in passing. It is the coloured kind which belongs to our story here—the soap-bubble. Perhaps the bypaths of light are nowhere more delightful than in this mode. As children we have all made soap-bubbles with a clay pipe and watched them ballooning above us. I did this of course; and when I did it I took the whole thing for granted, and without one-tenth the sense of mystery which I now possess. I am sure that I am by no means singular in this respect, in spite of the pundits with their famous 'child's sense of wonder' and heaven lying about us only in our infancy. I am sometimes told that I have retained my capacity to wonder. Yet this is not so: I have attained it. This is normal. It would be abnormal for a child to possess imagination instead of fancy. One might just as well expect the kid to have a mystic experience (which comes to few before the age of thirty-four).

The soap-bubble, like the water-drops of the rainbow, fans out the colours in the waves of light. It is worth watching this exhibit closely. If we are washing something and get a good froth of bubbles in the basin, and if that basin happens to be beside a latticed window, then what we behold is really striking. We look closely at one of the bubbles: the window is reflected on it in miniature, the bars pencilled with beautiful clarity: and this window now is coloured; we have a stained-glass window. And that is not all: this stained-glass window is continually changing its colours—just as if some wonderfully coloured scroll were being wound from behind by a fairy. The movement is caused by the unstable nature of the bubble whose envelope is shrinking and perishing. The result is a moving picture of changing colours until suddenly the screen splits and the film is over.

Our apparatus here, our experimental laboratory, is remarkably simple. So much so that perhaps the reader may think that though I disown the child's sense of wonder I am here unduly childish. Yet your Newton and Hooke, your Boyle and Young and Tyndall, were happy to blow soap-bubbles all day long—founding upon such an experiment theories (such as the Theory of Interference) of great practical importance. I should add that none of them seems to have been interested in or thought worthy of comment the little cinema show of the stained-glass windows which so appeals to me.

John Tyndall, being a nineteenth-century man, always wrote well, and I would like to quote his explanation of the soap-bubble phenomenon.

Whence, then, are derived the colours of the soap-bubble? Imagine a beam of white light impinging on the bubble. When it reaches the first surface of the film, a known fraction of the light is reflected back. But a large portion of the beam enters the film, reaches its second surface, and is again in part reflected. The waves from the second surface thus turn back and hotly pursue the waves from the first surface. And, if the thickness of the film be such as to cause the necessary retardation, the two systems of waves interfere with each other, producing augmented or diminished light, as the case may be.

But, inasmuch as the waves of light are of different lengths, it is plain that, to produce extinction in the case of the longer waves, a greater thickness of film is necessary than in the case of the shorter ones. Different colours, therefore, must appear at different thicknesses of the film.[1]

The soap-bubble is coloured then, not because it receives light like a flower but because, rainbow-like, it fans out the spectrum. I should add that the same is true concerning some clouds—we call them iridescent—which are coloured not in the manner of sunset and sunrise clouds, but by their own prism-work. The same is also true of some substantial things. The scales of butterflies and other flying insects bring out colours on the same principle, though to realize the extent and number of the lines a microscope is needed. The most famous example of what are called *striated surfaces* is that of mother-of-pearl. We are attracted by the lovely colours of that shell. Now it would be strange if that surface —all made of exactly the same calcareous substance—

[1] *On Light.*

rejected different wave-lengths at intervals. It would be as strange as if a leaf, all of the same substance, was not one colour (green) but many colours. We would doubt the whole theory of light. But the mother-of-pearl is not acting like an ordinary surface but in terms of a prism. The shell is composed of exceedingly thin layers which when cut across by the polishing of the shell expose their edges and furnish the necessary small and regular grooves. Some of the light is reflected from the grooves and some from the ridges, and by this interference the colour-rays become separated. This was first proved by Brewster who by stamping the shell carefully upon sealing-wax transferred the grooves and produced upon the wax all the colours of the mother-of-pearl. Taking his cue from this Barton made a machine to rule fine close lines upon steel buttons—which then shone and sparkled like diamonds in sun or gas-light.

Thus we see how the flimsy soap-bubble, the gentle rain, and the hard, incredibly tiled roofing of the pearl's palace, all alike work upon the waves of light.

iii

THE DROP

We have the sphere which is hollow—the bubble: and we have the sphere which is filled—the drop. It is a sphere of water full of water. That is strange. How does it achieve the globe? We would expect it to spread out if it is liquid. But it is a ball and shows no more signs of falling to pieces than if it were made of rubber. It will sometimes stay on a slanting surface, apparently stuck, though no ordinary ball could do this. It can even cling to the point of a thorn, hanging there as if with bracket or claw. This is due to 'surface tension'. I am a trifle weak on the law of surface tension and I will not ask you to join me in a study of it here. I am not weak in my admiration for the shining silver bead of rain-water lodged on the nasturtium leaf after a summer shower—I need gild it with no literary frill. As it hangs from the thorn or twig-end, it also will act as a prism. In the sunshine we may catch sight of it as a bright little lamp of amber, and then shifting our position see it change to blue—there is no prettier sight.

It also acts upon light in another way. It serves as a means by which the waves are squeezed closely together, especially those that produce heat. The paralleled rays are brought to a point at a given distance which we call the focus—another word for fire-place. The rays are so gathered at that point that we often find leaves singed by drops of water cupped upon them, while vases standing by a window have been known to set fire to the window-curtains. Since glass will behave in the same manner if constructed on the same lines as the drop, we have our burning-glasses, and in the Victorian era some gentlemen amused themselves by carry-ing a lens in their pockets to light their cigars with, while in many a stately home of England there were sun-dials in the garden so arranged with a lens and a little cannon that exactly at noon the rays would touch off the powder and the cannon would fire. If a burning-glass happens to be made of ice you can still make a fire. It is pleasing to get fire out of ice. Travellers in the Arctic regions in earlier centuries have astonished the natives in this way, for it is not easy or natural to conceive how warmth could be promoted by coldness.

The same reason which makes a drop or a lens act as a

burning-glass makes it act as a magnifying-glass. For inasmuch as the rays are brought together at a focal point, then beyond that point they will spread out and thus falsify the real size of the object.

In concluding it will be pleasant to remind ourselves by use of the very things we have been thinking about that a slab of ice, though so like glass, is made otherwise. It is composed of flowers: the ferns and fronds of crystal. We can take a block of common ice and turn it into a flower garden. Here is the block: behind it a light: in front of it a lens (which could be ice also): and in front of the lens a screen at a suitable distance. Thus:

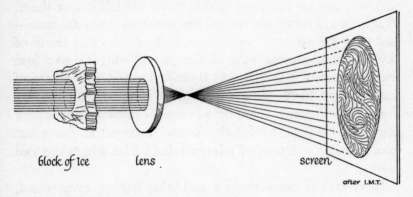

block of ice   lens   screen

after I.M.T.

And there on the screen is the flower garden.

iv

THE MIRAGE

The air itself can act like water and glass at times and so twist the waves of light that we fall into delusion and snare. When hot air causes *successive* bending of the rays in their

passage through the atmosphere we get strange effects:
then objects are displaced; that which is above is seen
below; that which is round the corner is in full sight—and
so on. Thus when a land surface is heated and there is what
is called a successive refraction we then see in the distance
not the land but the blue sky. It looks exactly like water.
We call it a mirage; and it is one of life's ironies that we are
inclined to see this phantom water precisely in those heat-
drenched arid places where the traveller most desires to find
it. The mockery of this cruel illusion is increased by the
extraordinary fact that if there are any high objects beyond
the supposed lake, such as trees or mountains, then they
will actually be reflected in this water which is not there.
The trees are there, the mountains are there, they are true—
and they are reflected in water which is false and made of
sky. Yet so complete is the illusion, so difficult is it to refuse
the evidence of our eyes that travellers while fully aware of
these things have often persisted in their belief until the
final disillusionment, and on a famous occasion the Deputy
Surveyor-General of South Australia reported the exact
geographical position of a large inland lake which did not
exist.

In certain circumstances a real lake, having evaporated,
will become the self-same piece of water again in the eye
of the unfortunate traveller. The author of *Eothen* tells of
such an experience. Journeying in the desert he came upon
the likeness of a fresh-water lake, a broad sheet stretching
deep into creeks and hemmed in by promontories. The shore-
line was so true and natural that he could not undeceive his
eyes till his camel had almost trodden in the seeming water.
'I soon saw the cause of this phantasm,' he says. 'A sheet
of water, heavily impregnated with salts, had gathered
together in a vast hollow between the sand-hills, and when

dried up by evaporation had left a white saline deposit; this exactly marked the space which the waters had covered, and so traced out a good shore-line. The minute crystals of the salt, by their way of sparkling in the sun, were made to seem like the dazzled face of a lake that is calm and smooth.'[1]

We can see a simple mirage on a hot day on any beach. One day, lying down on the Chesil Bank in Dorset, when the sun was so hot that the air was visibly quivering, I looked along the pebbles into the distance, my eyes being almost level with the ground. To my surprise I saw that the sea seemed to have come inland and then retreated leaving water in the shelf to the left of the bank along which I was looking. I saw some people walk through it without inconvenience or splashing—for that water was only light. The same kind of thing can often be seen by motorists on particularly good and level roads—lakes of water in front, not affecting any of the passers-by.

We must go out to sea in order to behold things which are round the corner, over the rim of the horizon—and yet visible. They are hooked up into the sky. This phenomenon is known as looming. The celebrated nineteenth-century navigator, Scoresby,[2] gives interesting examples of this, when rapid evaporation from the surface of the sea was taking place under a hot sun, thus causing great refraction. He would be sailing along in his ship, discerning nothing on the horizon and yet beholding a vessel far beyond the horizon resting in the air high above the water, upside-down. Sometimes he would see several images of this one ship together with multiple images of other ships, so that the distant sky seemed full of air-borne vessels sailing

[1] A. W. Kinglake: *Eothen*, Chapter XVII.
[2] See his *Greenland Voyage* and *Arctic Regions*.

upside-down. Such a sight was only possible in the evening when the slanting rays were bent round, and by the law of total internal reflection could act as ropes to hoist up the ships beyond the horizon into the direct sight of the sailors.[1]

Scoresby tells also how, under refractory conditions in the air, the coast would exhibit the most curious appearances. He would see great cities where no cities were. He would see unfolded before his eyes streets, monuments, and churches; the ruins of castles and obelisks; towering turrets, cloud-piercing minarets and spires. He would see hills surmounted with pinnacles and battlements, while others, subjected to another kind of refraction, would exhibit huge masses of rock lightly riding the air just above the topmost pile. The phantasmagorial exhibition, no sooner determined, would change into something else—an object being seen alternatively as a castle, a cathedral, or a pyramid, then expanding into a mighty bridge worthy to unite the creatures of earth with the hosts of heaven. 'These varied and sometimes beautiful metamorphoses', says Scoresby, 'naturally suggested the reality of fairy descriptions; for the air was perfectly transparent, the contrast of snow and rocks was quite distinct, even in the substance of the most uncommon phantasms, though examined with a powerful telescope, and every object seemed to possess every possible stability. I never observed a phenomenon so varied or so amusing.'[2]

In the deserts which contain mountains this particular kind of twisting of the real into the unreal can also be

[1] Captain John Budgell tells me that when passing south of the Isle of Wight he once saw Portsmouth upside-down in the air, and an aircraft-carrier suspended likewise above the water, while a landing aeroplane grounded wrong-side up and in opposition to the law of gravity!

[2] *Arctic Regions*.

witnessed. The traveller beholds, not the longed-for lake, but a glorious city looming clear before him like the fulfilment of a dream. More often in the deserts and arid plains things are merely modified or magnified; thus patches of gravel are turned into hills, or a low line of dwarfish scrub will be made to present the appearance of a forest on the edge of a big lake, every tree being distinctly reflected in the apparent water; camels are made to look like sheep, while farther on a flock of sheep are stretched into camels; a mere pile of stones along the track become ceaselessly plodding caravans; a distant hillock will seem to have become cut off from the earth and to be riding in the air completely detached. But the most usual thing is the old and terrible thing, the illusion of lakes near the horizon, the cause of bitter disappointment and too often responsible for the caravans which have been found full of the skeletons of those who had recklessly finished their supply of water. It is said that the animals are never deceived by a mirage, and perhaps this accounts for the disdainful look on the pessimistic faces of the camels.

CHAPTER FOUR

Phosphorescence

i

IN THE MINERAL

EVERY day the rays of the sun are cast upon the world giving it light and colour and causing these mirages and delusions. At night they are withdrawn and the earth is given over to darkness. Yet this is not wholly true. For, apart from the inconstant light of moon and stars, we can still behold the shining of many lamps which have not been made with hands.

This light comes from minerals, from gases and vapours, from plants, and from animals. The authorities have grouped it—rather loosely as it seems—under the general head of Living Light or Phosphorescence or Luminescence.[1]

Certain minerals possess the property of absorbing the rays of the sun by day to emit them by night. The first known example of such a mineral was barytine or Bologna Stone. We think of the cobbler, Vincenzo Cascariola, who about the latter end of the sixteenth century lived in a narrow street in the old town of Bologna. In the usual way of this world while seeking one thing he found another. He was devoted to alchemy and was always hunting for the means by which he might transmute base metal into gold.

[1] See E. Newton Harvey: *Living Light* and T. L. Phipson: *Phosphorescence.*

In his searches he came upon a very heavy stone (it was sulphate of baryta or heavy-spar) and he felt sure that here was a metallic ore from which he would ultimately be able to extract gold. He did not obtain gold. But by heating it with charcoal in a hot fire he extracted sulphuret of barium, a substance which shines in the dark after being exposed to the rays of the sun. That was the first mineral discovered to be luminescent after insolation. Since the Greeks called the morning star Phosphorus and the Romans called it Lucifer, the noun 'phosphorus' was given to the substance later found to be most luminescent and indeed inflammable. Thus the general term phosphorescent came to be applied to anything giving out light in this mode, while of course phosphorus enters into the composition of our common lucifer matches.

Bologna Stone is only one of the many minerals subject to phosphorescence. The list includes certain diamonds: glittering for us by day, they shine forth again at night. And it includes our common limestone. If a road which is strewn with bits of limestone has been open to a hot sun throughout a summer's day the traveller can do without a moon for the stones will be his lanterns. The sun has not only bounced off from the lime but got into it, and now in the night we get it back. In the West Country some chalky roads, steeply falling from a hill, look from a distance extremely like foamy waterfalls—I have caught sight of many such plunging into woods on a hill-side. If such a road faces south on a summer day it will soak up the sun. One night years ago, cycling through Dorset in the vicinity of Lyme Regis, I lost my way home, for it was very dark and I was off the main roads. (I did not mind this in the least and was delighted at the thought that one could still get lost in England as in the old days.) I was pushing on

through a very dark tree-closed vale when I saw a glow
coming from behind a group of trees in front. Evidently I
had reached a main road with lights. But no, it turned out
to be coming from my own road climbing steeply in front
of me. It had no lamps: it was a lamp—all of it palely glowing. No light from heaven fed the earth. It was the earth
which fed the sky. This lamp used no oil. It consumed
neither coal nor current. But it would shine so long as it
was fuelled by the darkness of the night.

So with some houses which have been whitewashed (or
limestone-washed). Such a house with a sun-trapping side
will glow in pitch darkness with quite a low candle-power
of light. During the war there were no more conscientious
(or angrier) citizens than Home Guardsmen. I knew one
such man—nearly always vexed in a moral and official
manner—who discerned again and again a glow coming
from a certain house at night when he was at a distance;
but when he got there he could see nothing but a white
house—for the glow was much more obvious from afar off.
Thus each time he was forced to go sorrowfully away, for
he had found no one to blame or to shout at.

I think it is right to say that these minerals achieve their
phosphorescence by virtue of the visible rays of the sun.
But a great many rays come from the sun which are not
luminous, not, as we say loosely, visible. Yet some of them
are very powerful. Thus the dark calorific rays exceed
many times in power the luminous solar rays. If they are
focused upon combustible bodies they will go up in
flames, some metals will be fused, others raised to the
temperature of whiteness. In this way the non-luminous
calorific rays are transformed into luminous ones yielding
all the colours of the spectrum. For this exhibit we use the
word Calorescence. So also with the ultra-violet rays—the

invisible ones beyond the violet. When they are focused upon certain substances they render them luminous in the dark: *invisible rays are thereby made visible.* The rays fall upon the object. They are not reflected back to our eyes so that we say—there is something bathed in light. They are absorbed: and having been absorbed the object becomes a lamp. But it is a cold lamp. It is an unburning fire. It is the spectre of flame fed with darkness and issuing out of blindness. This is called Fluorescence. Thus if the sun sent us no visible waves we would not sit in darkness but in ghostly light, for a great many minerals and organic compounds fluoresce—teeth and bones being especially brilliant. If we focus ultra-violet rays in the dark upon a man with a good set of teeth, if we fix a bone button on his collar, and ask him to smile, we will get such a good light that we can photograph him—getting a plate which will reveal a face in shadow with teeth and button blazing with light.

ii

IN THE AIR

Many of the atmospheric phenomena of light-emission are due to electric discharge. Thus the reports which have been made of luminescent raindrops and luminescent snow-flakes have generally been recorded after or during thunder-storms, as in the case of M. de Saussure who when travelling on the summit of the Breven claimed that fiery drops of rain splashed the coats and dripped from the hats of his companions in a waterfull of sparks. François Arago who was fond of collecting instances when the sky rained drops of fire instead of water tells how an ecclesiastic called Hallai who lived near Constance saw one evening during a thunderstorm 'rain which fell like drops of red-hot liquid metal'; how Bergman, a celebrated Swedish chemist, observed on two occasions 'rain which sparkled as it touched the ground making the latter appear as if covered with waves of fire'; and how the Abbé Bertholon on his way to Lyons was caught in a storm at five o'clock in the morning when hailstones striking against his horses' trappings burst into jets of flame.

Under the general head of meteorological phosphorescence a good many things have been listed including light from waterspouts, meteoric dust, shooting stars, clouds, mists, and fogs. The amount of things that cause atmospheric light is said to be the reason why on the darkest night there is always enough light for us to be able to make our way quite easily in open country as opposed to the stumbling blindness we experience in an unlit mine or cave. I suppose it also explains why snow still looks white in the dark— otherwise it should look black as ink.

The luminous mist known as Will-o'-the-Wisp or Jack-o'-Lantern or Ignis Fatuus is fairly well known. It is attributed to the inflammation of phosphuretted hydrogen gas and is sometimes seen over marshes, stagnant pools, and bogs. It is thought that the putrefaction of animal matters may promote it, and where the Will-o'-the-Wisp is observed in boggy lands it has been thought that it marked the spot where an unlucky traveller had been swallowed in the mire. In Wales they speak of 'corpse-candles' in graveyards. Such a light, rising from the green squelch of the frightful sinking grass in Ireland's bogs, has been taken for the ghost of someone who having stumbled in was sucked below.

The most famous instance of a luminous fog occurred at

Geneva in November 1859. During nine moonless nights a vast fog hung over the city and its neighbourhood, which diffused so much phosphoric light that people could read by it and travellers could see their way as if by the moon. Again, General Sabine, who once saw a luminous cloud hanging for nights on end amidst the lofty mountains which surround the Isle of Skye, was also a witness in company with Captain James Ross of an extraordinary appearance in the Greenland seas. Ahead of their vessel they saw *a stationary light* resting on the water and rising to a considerable height. Everywhere else was in darkness. When they sailed into the light the whole ship was so illuminated that they could discern the minutest portions of the rigging on the highest parts of masts and sails. It lasted for about four hundred and fifty yards. When they emerged they did so at once, going straight into darkness. Gazing astern they saw it now as one half of an illuminated arch standing on the sea, the other half coming down a good distance away. No satisfactory explanation has been given for this. As it is, it feeds the imagination—a great archway glowing in the blackness of night on the desolate waters; leading to nowhere; senseless, purposeless, glorious.

Sometimes a brush discharge of electricity during or in the wake of a thunderstorm will cause a tapering glow to appear on the spires of churches or even the tops of trees. It has been called St. Elmo's Fire and has most frequently been witnessed on the main-topgallant mast-heads of ships in open sea. Before the decline of religious and superstitious feeling such a sight was wont to cause alarm and awe among the mariners. Herman Melville, while reminding us that oaths to sailors are household words on most occasions whether in the trance of the calm or the teeth of the tempest, yet adds that in all his voyagings, 'seldom have I heard a

common oath when God's burning finger has been laid on
the ship; when His *Mene, Mene, Tekel Upharsin* has been
woven into the shrouds and the cordage'. The mighty
Melville was conjuring up before us one of those cosmic
pictures of which he is undisputed master. It was nearly the
eleventh hour of the *Pequod*'s chase. A typhoon had struck
the ship; had torn her canvas and left her bare-poled to face
the storm. When darkness came on, sky and sea roared and
split with thunder while elbowed lances of fire revealed the
disabled masts. It was then that gazing upward the affrighted
crew beheld all the yard-arms tipped with a pallid fire—
'Each of the three tall masts was silently burning in the
sulphurous air, like three gigantic wax tapers before an
altar.'

iii

IN THE PLANT

More than twenty plants are luminescent. Many of these
have red or orange-coloured flowers, such as the sunflower,
the marigold, the nasturtium, and the poppy. If we examine
them carefully in the evening after a hot day we shall see
sparks and flashes of miniature lightning fly forth. And
if we carry a green nasturtium leaf into a dark room
it will not be invisible, for a sort of moonlight will
inform it. Veins branch out from its centre to form a
star.

That light, that star which flickers on the flower came
from the sun. This is not true of all the plants which glow
in the dark. A large class of vegetation, the fungi, is
responsible for phosphorescence; but these are no lovers

of sunlight. They thrive in darkness. They feed in the fetid damp of lightless caves and cellars. The white flocenous extremities called the mycelia of the species known as R. *subterranea*, found in moist mines and caverns, evolve a tranquil phosphoric gleam pleasing to the traveller in these lone and desolate places, while sometimes the light is clear enough to read by. In the mines of Hesse in the north of Germany the walls of the galleries 'appear illuminated with a pale light resembling that of the moonbeams stealing through narrow crevices into some gloomy recess'.[1] If mouldy wood has fallen into the pot-holes so familiar to the spelæologists, phosphorescent mushrooms are often found growing upon it. On one expedition into the bowels of the earth, 326 feet down in the Moroccan Atlas, the French spelæologists, journeying through their endless night, came upon a meadow composed of thick white gleaming *grass*— suggestive of spectral hay fit for harvest only in the fields of hell.

Fungi of the more familiar kind flourish in the open, and the many examples of phosphorescent wood are all due to fungoid mycelium. 'No summer passes', says Harvey, 'without the discoveries of some phosphorescent wood, the fox-fire of English legend, often associated with elves and fairies. Old stumps of trees, moulding leaves, the inside of bark from logs on the ground will glow brilliantly and continuously, although actually cold.'[2] If we walk on an autumnal night through a wood—and every wood is primeval and eerie at that hour—push through the undergrowth, and stumble over rotting tree-trunks, it will be surprising if we come upon no such lowly light or elfish candle. It will be the effect of the tiny threads of mycelium

---

[1] T. L. Phipson: *Phosphorescence*.
[2] E. Newton Harvey: *Living Light*.

cells on the fungus. So too with luminous cheese or bread or potatoes. The light can be considerable on such, and we recall the celebrated occasion when a cellarful of potatoes in the barracks of Strasburg gave out such a blaze that the officer in charge gave the alarm that the place had caught fire.

iv

IN THE ANIMAL

The smallest lamps in the world are not mycelia but bacteria. They are responsible for the illumination we often get from decayed animal matter. This kind of cold light has been observed for some centuries, and the history of such discovery associates the name of Fabricius ab Aquapendente of Padua in 1592 with luminous mutton; Boyle claimed luminous veal, pig, and chicken in 1672; Beal came forward with fish in 1676; Paulinus with hen's eggs in 1707; and so on. The light given from flesh thus fuelled by bacteria is so considerable that it is often found possible to photograph a haddock, for instance, by its own luminosity.

Burning without fire these lamps will not call forth force. Thus before the Davy Lamp was invented for use in coal mines the lanterns were composed of luminous fish. It is a strange thought. It conjures up mystery upon mystery. In that place were crouching forces that would leap forward in answer to a flame. Silence; stillness; the blackness of dawnless night; nothing living, nothing moving—such is a corridor in a mine. No life is there—but force is sleeping there: animation is suspended in those inky halls. The entrapped sunshine is there—imprisoned for three hundred million years. A little flame will be enough to voice its presence. Strike a match—and suddenly that crunched and crouching power will leap out like a wild beast and rend the cage. So the early visitors to these lost forests of yesteryear were careful not to come with fire that would call forth the spirit of the ancient sun. The ineffectual flame they brought was cold and tame—a fireless torch upon a lifeless fish.

There are over forty kinds of light-producing animal. The more familiar ones are few, and most of them are insects. Moles, earthworms, and centipedes are said to give light, though I have not been fortunate enough to observe it personally, and I would certainly like to see Mr. Kanda's *Emplectonema* which gives the appearance of a green sinuous line of fire a metre in length which lights up at a touch, and the better known *Scolopendra electrica* which has one hundred and forty legs attached to a body which looks like a train with light shining from seventy windows. We have all seen the beetle called the glow-worm. Though common it holds just as much magic as the more exotic and unusual. We are glad to come upon it glowing in the grass by the side of our path, or shining lighthouse-lonely on a prostrate bark. Put it close to print and you can read the letters. A glassful gives us the ghost of a lamp. But, strictly, it does not hold a candle to the glow-worm of the West Indies, the famous 'cucujo' beetle with two bright green lights on front of the thorax and an orange one on the abdomen. The early travellers in the West Indies maintained that the natives used a collection of these beetles as effective lamps in their huts and as torches tied to their feet to light up the forest paths at night; that lovers presented their girls with the living gems which shone from their hair in the dark; that on festival days the youths tied numbers of the beetles to their garments and rushed through the streets, while others, rubbing their faces with the flesh of dead 'cucujos', scared the neighbours with their flaming countenances. In the Tropics these luminous creatures, when sometimes massed in the distance, throw out a remarkable amount of light. They have been mistaken for the lights of a town or village. During the early days of colonization and imperial progress they have given the impression of an advancing army, before which the British soldiery, taken by surprise, have made a strategic retreat.[1]

Kindred to the cucujos are the fire-flies which are especially prolific in the Tropics, though fine displays are seen in temperate North America from May to July. In Japan they are still bought and sold as a commercial undertaking, and a fire-fly festival used to be held on Lake Biwa when merrymakers who had rowed out would free their pets from cages at a given signal to fly high above the water and the shore, and there were pleasing occasions when ten thousand fire-flies would be liberated before the palace of the Emperor as a token of the people's affection. The dance of the fire-flies is one of the outstanding sights of Siam. Coming out of the forest they select certain trees, perhaps extending for a quarter of a mile along the bank of a river. Harvey maintains that their strange flashing may continue hour after hour, night after night for weeks or even months, though he does not say whether they take it in turns to rest or whether all of them perform these rites without food or sleep in pauseless chase. They act with an extraordinary synchronism: their light blazes and is extinguished by a common sympathy. The spectator sees them sport in countless multitudes round a favourite tree

[1] See Amy Johnson: *Sunshine*, p. 300.

to produce a magnificent illumination. 'At one moment every leaf and branch appears decorated with diamond-like fire,' says Sir John Bowring, 'and soon there is darkness, to be again succeeded by flashes from innumerable lamps which whirl about in rapid agitation.'

Some authorities have assumed that this turning on and off of lights is a mating signal, for such sexual signals have been clearly observed in action between glow-worms. But these flies in the tree are said to be all male, while the females afar off are wingless. So the theory hardly works. We should more rightly assume that just as the peacock does not in the least need all those feathers to attract the hen, so here again in the dance of the fire-flies we should not look for some simple intention pleasing to insect specialists, but rather accept an Exhibition with no purpose save life and no reason save joy.

The authorities are not yet certain in every case as to the agent of illumination—whether bacterial or chemical. In many cases it is a chemical action between the constituents of luciferin and luciferase, the energetic agent being oxidization; while in others it is purely bacterial. It is certainly not easy to determine a supposed luminous form from truly luminous organisms living on it when the light of the former is purely secondary. However, I understand that the case of luminous fleas can be simply referred to bacteria, as also the occasional illuminated caterpillar, termite, spider, and those legionary ants who advancing through the forest in phalanxed millions like a flood on fire overcome all who try to stay their march and petrify the stoutest heart. But larger animals on land are seldom luminescent, and those luminous frogs observed by Harvey in Cuba, with an intense light shining through their bellies, had just finished a hearty meal of fire-flies.

V

IN THE SEA

At the close of his account of the Cataracts of the Orinoco in his *Aspects of Nature*, Humboldt speaks of the countless insects that 'poured their red phosphoric light on the herb-covered ground, which glowed with living fire as if the starry canopy of heaven had sunk down upon the turf'. Yet it is not the fiery flies of the East, nor the massed mycelia of the fungi glowing upon the rotting barks of fallen trees, nor yet the bacteria that illuminate their living hosts, which provide the most splendid spectacle of earthly light. It is a mere speck of jelly smaller than a pin's head which gives the greater glory witnessed on the sea. The *Noctiluca Millaris*, or Night-Light, when very much magnified looks like a peach with a long stalk, which it wags about and pushes against objects that come in its way. In its body are little points of light which rapidly appear and disappear. In some parts of the world twenty-five thousand of these creatures can be found in a cubic foot of sea-water. When the whole of an area is thus covered we have a memorable sight. The Red Sea is such a soup of *Noctiluca* that it derives its name from their hue. They are more often seen in the warmer seas, and we read many descriptions of it, from Father Bourges, who in 1704 said that 'on the Coast of Brazil the Shore was one Night so very bright that it appeared as if it had been on Fire', to Darwin's sober observation in his *Voyage of the Beagle*—'While sailing a little south of the Plata on one very dark night, the sea presented a wonderful and most beautiful spectacle. There was a fresh breeze, and every part of the surface, which during the day is seen as foam, now glowed with a pale light. The vessel drove before her bows billows of liquid phosphorus, and in her wake she was followed by a milky train.'

Europeans need not go so far afield to witness phosphorescence. It is quite common in the English Channel, and Phipson claims that he found *Noctiluca* in such prodigious numbers in the damp sand in Ostend that, on raising a handful of it, it appeared like so much molten lava. It is by no means rare in the south of Ireland. Many years ago, on a hot summer evening, I went to bathe with my brother[1] on the coast of Kerry. We turned out of a dark lane to a bay, with crags at each end of the horse-shoe. It was a very dark night. At such times water looks blacker than the darkness—an element most alien and fearful. What we saw now, coming suddenly from the lane, was very different. As the waves fell lightly on the shore they broke in scrolls of phantom fire. The crags looked like ships floating on a sea of flame whose waves broke in sparks before their prows. Some fishermen were at work, whose nets beneath the water looked like silver webs and the wriggling fish like tongues of writhing flame. Their oars dripped fire into the fire. We waded out into it and we encountered a seal with phosphorescent whiskers. I saw my brother as a man in flames—not feeling it. I looked at my arm—it was a firebrand. Above, the dark night implacably roofed us. It was as if we were being shown that life calls for light and must needs be linked with it, and that here again, as with bacteria, as with mycelia, the humblest of all the children of earth are seen to assault and prevail against the powers of night.

We go beneath the waves. We get hold of a balloon in

[1] Dr. Robert Collis.

reverse, and instead of going up into the sky we go down into the sunless depths of the sea. We can do this today. We are accustomed now to being housed in the air, and housed on the surface of the sea; but beneath the waves—a house there? Yet, as we know, even this is possible now, and we turn to Beebe and Barton, the magicians in this sort, and they give us a balloon or bathysphere, and down we go in a room large enough for two, with a window of fused quartz able to withstand thirty-five tons of pressure.

We descend—and gaze from our window at the apparitions that glide before our eyes. We pass away from the world. When we fly into the air, though we have no footing there we yet belong to earth, and can see the earth, and are bathed in glorious light. When we enter into the caverns of the world, the pot-holes going on for miles, though dedicated to darkness they are still the territory of man—even in those dungeoned lands he is no trespasser. But when we have gone down deep below the surface of the sea, we feel scarcely human. It is as if we were disembodied spirits, or just an eye, a consciousness, brooding upon worlds unrealized by the living soul.

These regions have known no day. And therefore no day following the night, no break in timeless dark. The waves of light sent out by the sun can pierce through the water only for a certain distance. The red ones, being larger, have a lesser frequency than the smaller, so red fades first and a scarlet scarf turns black by forty feet down; by two hundred feet orange and yellow will have gone. At last we are left with a velvety blue-black—think of it!—in the Pacific, on, on, and on, and still no end of it.

When we go Everest-high into the air we see no animal-life from our window, no strange birds flit to and fro outside. When we go Everest-low beneath the waves, animals known and unknown, named and unnamed, continually pass before us, forms so strange that if they did not exist it would be unnecessary to invent them—nay, impossible. Sealed inside our window in the deep, a speck of consciousness, an eye among the blind keeping watch upon the extravagant and erring shapes of primal life, we may well see some that were posted here since the foundation of the world. Such, perhaps, is the *Linophryni arborifer* or deep-sea devil-fish. Through what wild centuries roves back its lineage? On its nose is built a lamp-post, the lamp alight and gently waving in the water; from its chin a tree grows downwards, many-branched: its body is chiefly head; its head is chiefly mouth—a phosphorescent cavern with teeth for stalagmites and stalactites, an open invitation to every witless fish that comes wandering by. It disappears, and in its place we see—a motor-car? Anyway it has two head-lamps which it turns on and off. This is the *Photoblepharan palpelratus* which harbours a bag of bacteria under each eye in the equilibrium called symbiosis. When it passes from our sight we do not peer into total darkness (in any case we carry our night-piercing artificial eye, a very powerful searchlight) but rather into a firmament thick with stars which move about and go in and out, for almost half of the inhabitants are luminous. A dozen parachutes go by, their umbrellas all lit up; and then suddenly there is a silent explosion as when fireworks make a pattern in the sky—has some creature burst into a shower of sparks? It is a prawn which has expelled a volume of luminous matter in order to conceal itself from a pursuer, just as in the light above a squid will exude ink for the same purpose. A very furry caterpillar passes, simply blazing with light: this is the polynoid sea-worm. It is in trouble, the usual trouble of being about to be eaten; so it sacrifices part of itself, its tail, which is unhinged while the front portion of its body, ceasing to luminesce, goes off in safety to grow a new tail. Then we see a long sack with a luminous red whip attached to it: this is the pelican eel which can swallow creatures larger than itself.

We sit at our window gazing out into a world that never ceases to flash with light from tiny pin-heads in their masses to huge long fishes some looking exactly like liners with rows of illuminated port-holes. It is difficult to understand why these animals are thus lit up. In this instance and in that it seems to serve a useful purpose, but often it appears as an unnecessary advertisement of presence to the enemy, and here we see nothing but enmity—nothing. The answer has not yet been found to this question. All we know as we sit at our window as if we were the spies of God trying to make sense of His own world, all we know is that here, even here, in this first layer of life, exiled from the sun, there is Light.

PART II

Man and Light

CHAPTER ONE

The Story of the Lamp

i

LIGHTING

THE earliest of primitive men knew only one source of light and heat—the sun. They did not know that when its rays are withdrawn the earth itself can give light. They did not know that nearly every single thing can be turned into sun. They did not know that without using up any substance by turning it into flame they could yet have abundant light leaping out of darkness.

There is a tendency to think of modern times as outstanding in terms of noise and machinery; yet a visitor from any past age between, say, 2500 B.C. and the latter part of the nineteenth century, would probably be most struck by the lights. For lighting remained primitive till then—strange but true. We stuck almost as cave-men in this till only the other day. Now we live in such a blaze that we can hardly credit the fact. Yet our particular generation can grasp the difference, for when progress brought the last war we were obliged to return to earlier eras and to comprehend again the meaning of darkness. We called it the 'black-out' which was quite a good word to describe it and a good symbol of the state of affairs—though symbols are not always so straightforward, and our modern excess of light does not mean that we are now excessively enlightened.

We do not know what tribe lit the first fire or who plucked the first brand from the burning as a torch; but the imagination plays happily upon the thought of first occasions—especially upon this thought. For this particular first occasion so signally marks our separation from the animals. It is so natural to think of a man, however primitive, doing it. It is so unnatural to think of any animal, however long its species lived, doing it. It pleases us to imagine the first time a brand was used as a portable light. The word 'torch' appeals to us still; it is so soaked in the history of our battle with the dark that we prefer to use it even when electric flash-light should be the term, while a torch is carried from hand to hand across Europe when under the sign of the Olympic Games the athletes of all nations exhibit the flame of youth.

After the rough flaming fagot came the splinter. It was long and straight and so satisfactory in a simple way that it was used in parts of Scotland till the beginning of this century. After the splinter, the rushlight. Rushes were cut, stripped, dried, and then dipped into scalding grease. A reed two feet long, stuck in a holder, would burn for an hour. They were still in use when Gilbert White wrote his *History*, and he mentions how eleven rushes with half an hour's light in each could be bought for a farthing.[1] After the rushlight, the candle. It was an improved rushlight made by the repeated dipping of a fibre wick into a tub of molten wax or tallow. The candle is with us still. It has made way

---

[1] Indeed, 'the farthing candle' was a term synonymous with cheapness well into the nineteenth century, as witnessed by Charles Lamb's remark:

> Some cry up Haydn, some Mozart
> Just as the whim bites. For my part
> I do not care a farthing candle
> For either of them, nor for Handel.

for other things, but it does not pass. Time cannot blow it out. It is too happy an invention—a fuel that will not upset if we put it in pocket or suitcase. At times we need the pale comfort of its æsthetic appeal—and nothing lasts so well as art. The village in which I live in Surrey is so swamped by suburbia that I cannot buy an oil-lamp in any shop—but there are candles in abundance.

So to lamps. I try to be chronological—for I must get from one thing to another in as pleasing a manner as possible in this little history lesson. But the chronology defeats even our light-experts and lamp-fanciers. So much has happened simultaneously, or gone out of order, or even backwards at times. Thus excavations of the Royal Tombs at Ur revealed, among other impedimenta including the bones of servants who committed suicide on the death of kings, the existence of gold lamps with wick channels; but there were subsequently long periods, as during the Middle Ages, when though lamps had been invented, people seem to have reverted to candles. In any case progress in the sense of steady improvement of illuminants is absent from this subject. 'There was remarkably little progress', says Mr. O'Dea, 'from the early dynastic period at Ur (which ended before 2500 B.C.) to the latter part of the eighteenth century A.D. Forms of lamp unearthed at Ur have appeared and reappeared at intervals all over the world with every probability that most reappearances were unconnected with the ones before. The Greeks and Romans knew nearly as much about lighting as was known in the eighteenth century, and even at the beginning of the nineteenth century the Eddystone light was still provided with candles.'[1] Startling words—fully supported by other historians of the subject.

[1] W. T. O'Dea: *Darkness Into Daylight*.

The first lamps were fat-lamps—not oil. In the Old Stone Age, it is supposed, primitive men, sitting round a fire observed a bit of moss or lump of hair burning away on its own in a hollow stone filled with fat—the remnant of some carcass they had been cooking. It is thought that this is the way the 'oil'-lamp was born in Europe, America, and Asia. And indeed these ready-made hollows, whether of stone or skull or sea-shell made such simple serviceable lamps that they persisted up till recent times here and there, some being in use in the Shetland Islands late in the nineteenth century. Unless the stone lamps had some kind of ledge or lip so that they could be lifted without too much discomfort they can never have been as pleasant as the delightful shell lamps which in any case provided a deeper well for the liquid fat. It is a little difficult to see how the 'wick' worked on these occasions, but there was no difficulty when the Stormy Petrel was used—a most popular form of lamp at one time —for the wick was threaded through the beak and fed with the fat in the body.

It is interesting to note how the sea has aided our illumination: the sea-shell, the sea-bird, and then the sperm whale for its oil. For after the fat-lamp we come to the oil-lamp. The sperm whale provided large quantities of oil. Its head is a living cistern. It is a well of milky oil deep enough to fill a hundred buckets. And so the whale, the godly leviathan, the most splendid and harmless of all creatures, must be hunted and butchered for the benefit of the most savage. Luckily for it other creatures also took on the job of supplying us with oil—creatures on a scale of minuteness equal to the whale on its scale of hugeness, the planktonic crustaceans of the ocean. 'The energy in the petrol which drives our motor and flying age', says Professor Alister Hardy, 'is derived from that originally trapped from the sunlight by the tiny planktonic plants in the seas of long ago. According to current geological theory, the great supplies of mineral oil have been formed, in the course of ages, from the remains of marine organisms buried in sedimentation.'[1] Stranger than the Cliffs of Dover bricked by the shells of globigerina; stranger than coal which is sunshine fused with fossilized forest—is this further digging up of old sunshine consolidated by marine organisms in the depths of the sea, eventually to be found after the shifting of the waters under the plains and the deserts of the earth. They went down, these little things, these plant-creatures, they lay down in their massive millions to rest peacefully for evermore. They have risen from the dead—as oil. From oil they have changed into light and speed—and also, how well we know it!—into endless conflict of nations and the graves of men dying in the cause of commerce.

To rise as oil. That called not for man's savagery but for the sublime audacity of his imagination. It was in 1859 that Colonel E. L. Drake discovered oil in Pennsylvania. By studying the geological formations he concluded that mineral oil could be obtained by boring. 'To his imagination,' says Luckiesh, 'which saw vast reservoirs of oil in the depths of the earth, the world owes a great debt.'[2] Having obtained oil and refined it for burning we were then free to summon to our aid the law of capillarity, at work day and night among the plants, by virtue of which a fluid will flow upward against gravity in the channel of a root or a wick. Thus the oil-lamp came into existence. Nevertheless for a long time it gave but a poor light. The combustion was less complete than that of a candle, with the resultant smoke— which is simply the flying off of the bits and pieces not

[1] *The Open Sea: the World of Plankton.*
[2] M. Luckiesh: *Artificial Light.*

transmuted into pure flame. The value of an upward draught had occurred to Leonardo da Vinci in the fifteenth century, and in 1784 Argand one day stuck the broken neck of a bottle over a lighted wick and was surprised by the improved flame, but it was not till nearly a century later that glass chimneys were introduced, thus at once strengthening and sheltering the former feeble light.

After the oil-lamp, the gas-light—though not to the exclusion or elimination of the former. 'It is now nearly sixteen years', wrote William Murdock in 1808 in the Philosophical Transactions of the Royal Society of London, 'since, in a course of experiments I was making at Redruth in Cornwall upon the quantities and qualities of the gases produced by distillation from different mineral and vegetable substances, I was induced by some observations I had previously made upon the burning of coal, to try the combustible property of the gases produced from it.' In his first trial he burned the gas at the open ends of pipes, then improved on this by closing the ends and boring small holes from which the gas flames diverged, and subsequently improved on that after using his wife's thimble in an emergency to close the end of a pipe—for the worn thimble contained a number of tiny holes serving as excellent jets. After due digestion and delay gas-lighting became familiar in the nineteenth century and was carried on well into the twentieth. As a boy I lit my bedroom in this way, a fish-tail of light answering my match. It didn't intrigue me much at that age, but I did like watching the man in the street going from post to post with his lighting-rod in the dusk. By that time improvements had brought in the gas-mantle and the oil-lamp mantle and so on. Anyone with a turn for museum-knowledge should derive satisfaction from Mr. Robins's 354 illustrations of the various forms of lamp introduced in our long struggle against the dark until we had turned night into day.[1]

After gas-light, electric light. Since in this book electricity does not belong to the main region of my song I must take it as given and only acknowledge the fact that its current will run swiftly along a wire, and if the wire is made to offer resistance then that force will make the molecules move so fast that the wire will become red-hot and white-hot. Anything which impedes the flow of electricity will cause light. I suppose we all have favourite examples of this. Mine is the electric train going through snow. Quite recently when travelling up to London on an electric railway during a snowstorm I witnessed a striking display of this kind. The train was obliged to go by fits and starts, slowly picking its way through the snow-covered track. I put my head out of the window into the driving snow and was most unwilling to draw it back on account of what I saw. As the engine moved forward dazzlingly white incandescence would leap from the wheels with a great hiss and illuminate the countryside as if with sheet-lightning. The spluttering blaze issuing from the snow-crunching wheels made a powerful sight: darkness; snow-crystals; electricity—and out of these the leaping light!

How control, cabin, and confine this current? It had been studied since the seventeenth century by the men of genius who could see: it was made serviceable in the nineteenth and twentieth centuries by the men of genius who could apply—for the discoveries of the scientific explorer usually antedate by many years the applications derived from the trophies he has exhibited to the inventor. First came the Arc-Lamp. It was known that metal when made white-hot by electricity gave out a good light—but a wire

[1] See his *The Story of the Lamp.*

at white heat melted away. Davy came forward and showed how two pieces of carbon three inches apart and attached to the terminals of a battery gave a glaring light which did not burn the sticks. These arc-lamps could be used for the streets but not for houses. So to Moleyn, Edison, and Swan. They demonstrated how mere threads or fibres were sufficient if protected by a vacuum within a glass bulb. A flame goes *out* if it has no oxygen. This flame keeps *in* if it has no oxygen. For though it gives light it is not really a flame, it is not fire, it is not combustion, it is not transmutation—it is only heat made visible. We trapped lightning and put it in a cage of glass. We obtained an unadulterated light as pure and silent as if it were a globe of sunshine, without deleterious gases or noxious vapours or smoke, indifferent alike to storm or lack of air, more constant than the cloud-conditioned sun—and cheaper than oil.

To produce this took time. 'Thirty years in the life of a brilliant investigator such as Swan', says Mr. O'Dea, 'may seem excessive for the solution of a problem so apparently simple in its final answer as the carbon filament lamp. It is, however, almost axiomatic in science that the simplest results are often the most difficult to demonstrate, and what appeared to be just a strip of carbon in a glass envelope had behind it a genealogy involving many of the best scientific brains of the time.' In the present day, when everything is taken for granted (and even as a 'right'!) such a remark goes unheeded. A hundred years ago a lighthouse used ordinary candles. Today Eddystone Lighthouse has some 100,000 candle-power, while Ryan's Searchlight casts abroad a beam of 2,600,000,000 candle-power. It is all accepted with indifference as a matter of course.

We are spoilt on account of the too sudden, complete, and swift technical advance. For thousands and thousands of years mankind, while offering a great variety of civilization in dress and custom and culture, seems to have remained much the same basically till the nineteenth century. The Chinese made gunpowder but only used it for fireworks; the Japanese discovered luminescence without doing anything about it; the power of steam was obvious for centuries to all who ever watched a boiling kettle; Leonardo da Vinci had grasped a variety of mechanical principles without much interesting anyone, and so on. Then comes a change of attitude. It was a change from philosophizing to investigating Nature and organizing knowledge; the periods of pure philosophy gave way to methodical research, the discovery of the network of natural laws, and hence to the birth of physics and chemistry. When this happened the lurch forward into modern times was very sudden, everything seemed to happen at once, and our age *does not know* what it was really like living in earlier times, though in many basic ways a visitor from hundreds of years before Christ would get no great shock if he could sit down one evening in an eighteenth-century house or cottage. Then there is the swift drive onward into mechanization and industrialism utterly dividing us from the past while leaving us free to wonder how far our B.B.C. souls are in advance of B.C. ones.

We live in an age when the masses not only take all the works and wonders of Nature for granted but also the achievements which give them comfort and luxury on every side. Speaking of the new man, the modern man, in his *Revolt of the Masses*, Ortega y Gasset points out how limitation, obligation, dependence, pressure, even oppression cosmic and social, was what life meant to men up to only a hundred years ago, or the date at which the limitless expansion of scientific technique began. 'Previously, even for the rich and powerful, the world was a place of poverty, difficulty, and danger', and he notes that however rich an individual might be in relation to his fellows in former ages, 'since the world in its totality was poor, the sphere of conveniences and commodities with which his wealth furnished him was very limited. The life of the average man today is easier, more convenient and safer than that of the most powerful in another age. What difference does it make to him not to be richer than others if the world is richer and furnishes him with magnificent roads, railways, telegraphs, hotels, personal safety and aspirin?' It all leads to modern massman's fundamental traits of 'radical ingratitude towards all that has made possible the ease of his existence', an ingratitude which expresses 'the well-known psychology of the spoilt child'.

The extreme instance of this is the manner in which he turns on with a single movement of forefinger and thumb the radio and television with complete indifference and ignorance and lack of sense of privilege and responsibility. The same with the electric-light switch—though if 'the current' fails in a big city in a time of crisis he is more helpless than any savage. I wonder how many of us ever bother to have a look at the lighting outfit inside a bulb—say, when the filament is broken and we have to throw it away. It is worth looking at: a glass pillar topped by a thin neck, two wires clearly seen inside the glass protrude at a certain point like antennæ, the tips of which are laced with the filament. I could describe it by saying that if it were copied exactly on a larger scale it might win a prize at a modern sculpture exhibition if labelled 'Unknown Airman' or 'N.A.T.O.' If, somehow, we had never seen a bulb, and said, 'I'd like one of these,' and if the reply came from a knowledgeable person showing it, 'Yes, but I'm afraid they are rather expensive—still I might be able to get you one for ten pounds,' we would think it a bargain. Until 1915 bulbs were made by two workers using a blow-pipe and a pot of molten glass and shaped by hand—rather a delightful and creative job. Today, as one of the results of what may fairly be called the fanaticism of industrialism, the Westlake Machine, imitating the hand process, produces 100,000 bulbs every twenty-four hours—the former two workers, or their similars, being now engaged perhaps in making some portion of a Westlake Machine or in waiting upon one.

After the arc-lamp and the filament lamp came modifications and expansions such as discharge lamps, and the artificial fluorescence called neon lighting, and the successes of flood-lighting, and the marvels of the modern lighthouse. Thus what we see today is remarkable enough. It is night-time: the rays of the sun have been withdrawn from our quarter of the earth. And yet it shines. The streets of New York are as bright as by day. We gaze at Piccadilly, or at Luna Park in Coney Island laced with sixty thousand little suns. All of that light has been pumped up like oil out of the earth itself.

ii

SINS AGAINST LIGHT

Writing at the age of ninety-two, L. P. Jacks in his *Near the Brink* recalls a psychological experiment conducted with a view to testing the observational power of a group of young people. They were given five minutes in a well-furnished room and asked to record what they had observed. Afterwards one of the assessors said to him: 'Isn't it strange that not one of these observers, not even the best, has mentioned *the light* as one of the objects present in the room, or as having anything to do with the matter?' And Jacks comments that in his twenties he also would have overlooked the light, but that being in his nineties it would be the first thing to be observed. 'Is it a profane thought', he asks, 'that you can instantly fill a dark room with the "bright effluence"[1] of the Living God by turning an electric switch? If so, I confess to that profanity. I tell my young friend with his private aeroplane that Edison invented a finer thing than that.' Personally, though neither in my twenties nor nineties I find myself strongly influenced by the way a room is lighted, and am inclined to write off any man's claim to taste or sensibility if he over-lights his rooms—since harsh light is as bad as the over-loud blare on the radios of the uneducated.

Possibly the Americans are more in advance here. In their houses lamps are placed tastefully in every corner giving out as pleasing and comfortable a light as in the old days of oil-lamps—with never a blaze of white light from the ceiling. Certainly it is in America that most effort is being made to think of lighting as an art. They go in for it in a big way. A 'light-expert' is called in, often succeeding where psychiatrists have failed. For to be a light-specialist is also to be a colour-specialist, and I have come upon amusing examples of therapy in this mode when wives, unaccountably 'in the blues', have been completely restored in the affections of their husbands by the simple expedient of changing the colour scheme of the home. Much research is carried out on the whole subject, it being now discovered that Nature's work should be improved upon and that in any case daylight is too expensive since it costs over six

[1] 'Bright effluence of bright essence increate'—*Paradise Lost.*

hundred dollars in seven-roomed houses—the money going on windows. As for the factories, all sorts of light and colour theories are advanced with a view to the increase of production, and since it has been found that workers complain of being cold when the factory-walls are blue, they are changed to yellow whereupon workers feel comfortably warm, and so on. The same sort of research has also been conducted in England. We need not attach too much importance to it. I recall a story told by Lord Geddes in the House of Lords. He related how in a certain factory a group of researchers earnestly got to work for months. They turned down the lights. Production increased. They turned up the lights. Production increased. They softened the lights. Production increased. They turned them up and down again. Production increased. At length they reached the conclusion that production increased—when personal interest was taken in the workers.

When we look round and observe how lights are sometimes used in modern times, we are not always able to preserve our equanimity. In London there are a number of places called Milk Bars—why exactly named no one knows. Entering one recently, I asked for some tea and was given a cup—of a liquid which looked the colour of celery soup. 'That will be ninepence, dear,' said the attendant (she called me 'dear' not because she liked me but because she didn't want to call me 'sir'). Since it was not a draught calculated to elevate my drooping spirits, I asked for a sandwich. Using a little pair of tongs, she took hold of something gingerly as if it were a dangerous substance she wasn't going to risk touching, and handed it to me on a plate. I had a look at its contents by lifting the upper lip of white bread, and saw a very thin piece of what looked like pink skin lying there on its doughy bed like a guilty thing surprised. Dare I eat it? I glanced round at the other people, and seeing that they were all munching some similar object as if it were nutriment, I swallowed mine without immediate ill-effect. However, all this is by the way; what really appalled me, what appals me always in these places, was the quality of the lighting. A glaring blaze of un-covered lights beat down mercilessly upon us all: about on a par with the amount in an actor's dressing-room (which even there is probably only an absurd and unnecessary tradition). Nor man nor boy, nor youth nor age could take it. It was not the worst which I have come across in such places: here, there, and elsewhere I have known it to be viler still, that particularly foul strip imitation daylight which corrupts every countenance beyond endurance. Why do the proprietors do this? I think they do it on purpose, I think they thus promote the greatest unhappiness of the greatest number of their clients in order to make them leave immediately after their meal, and so make way for others.

It is not done everywhere with malice-aforethought. It is often due quite simply to tastelessness and ignorance. There is a certain public house in the Docks of London on the south side of Rotherhithe Street to which over many years I have been accustomed to take friends who are only familiar with the set pieces of the city. It overlooks the river. From its balcony you look straight down upon the water. At full tide the traffic gushes past below, in the evening with the red and green lights upon the ships. I know nothing more appealing than this sight; the heart of man and nature beating together; while beauty, unarranged and uninvited yet drenches the whole scene with mystery and resolves the seeming discord of our struggle by the revelation of harmony. The inside of the pub used to be much like any other—not startlingly offensive. I brought two American

friends there last year. A new manager had taken over. All
was changed. On entering the place it was as if one were
knocked sideways by a strong wind or deafened by a blare
of noise, for the new manager had put in dozens of blazing
bare lights—two dozen at least stuck on the ceiling. The
wretched man had spent big sums of money in making these
modern improvements, only to make it hateful. I glanced
round at the workmen in the bar; they all looked as dejected
as horses standing in the rain—they all hated it without
knowing why. But this kind of thing passes unnoticed
now, it so much belongs to our time. And by God, the
harshness, who can measure the harshness of our day! I
peeped into a cow-shed recently on a cold winter's eve. And
did I see what used to be seen for hundreds of years—cows
in their stalls attended by more than one milkman or maid,
lantern beside, head leaning against the warm animal, hands
milking? Of course not: the machine milker was going full
tilt with its machine noise, and electric light blazed across—
the stalls?—no, asphalted pens, hell to contemplate. And set
there in the midst—one soured and lonely girl. Need I say
that as I write I see the faces of the half-hearted, half-
mental utilitarian democrats, bringing out with slot-
machine automatism, their penny baby-word—Sentimental.
Don't I know that it saves time and that it saves money
and saves staff? True, but what does it do for humanity?
Fancy thinking of *that*! Humanity is nothing, human lives
are nothing, the burning hearts and the souls that yearn
above all for companionship are nothing, have nothing to
do with economics. And fancy implying that work need
not always be something to get finished as soon as possible
to make way for leisure and play. And so the modern cow-
sheds and all the rest of it multiply and multiply and men
everywhere are exchanged for metal. When Jesus was born

there was no room in the inn, they say. It did not matter. There was the stable, the stable of old-time. And the gentle beam that beat upon the boy shines still.

The undim, irreligious light of electricity is now entering the churches. The bulbs are shaped in the aspect of candles—than which nothing could be more grotesque. True candles are what we must have in churches. For they alone cast the light which we know to be religious. We can hear nothing in a blare of noise. We can see nothing in a blaze of light. Is it any wonder that in this age the voice of God which comes not as a roaring mighty wind but is so small and still, should be heard so seldom? And we may be very sure that it is not the illumination from electricity that will help to kindle that other light, the inner light which rises out of stillness, out of silence, out of darkness, and which when all is said is the light that lighteneth every man who cometh into the world.

Scarcely more than a hundred years ago people were afraid to venture into the city streets after dark. No rich man, it used to be said, went out before making his will, so numerous and ferocious were the brigands. It is different today. We are taken care of by the modern shields of light. When they are extremely modern, in England anyway, where things are always brought fanatically to excess, the price we have to pay for it is interesting.

I remember the first evening this was brought home to me as I walked through a completely modernized street. My way was along London's Euston Road towards St. Pancras Station. The first person to pass me was an old man. He looked terribly ill. He was walking slowly and unsteadily; I was distressed by the exceeding pallor of his face and I wondered whether he would be able to reach his destination on foot. Then two rather rough-featured men went by walking rapidly; both of them were evidently also a prey to some dreadful disease, for their faces had lost all healthy colour and were a dirty grey-green, disturbing to contemplate. A couple of lovers followed—and they too had been stricken down. The features of the girl were well-formed but she did not put me in mind of the lily or the rose, for her illness made her ugly; and it was just as well, I thought, that her companion was likewise a victim of this scourge, and indeed he might have risen from the tomb, so ghastly was his hue. I wondered what they privately thought of one another's skin. Others passed: people who had sustained some awful shock perhaps or come from a scene of crime in deadly fear. Had some blight fallen upon the city? Then I saw my own hands—and found that they also were foul to look upon. So I realized at last that the ravaged countenances were all caused by the modern street-lighting.

What are we to make of this? We can never escape the significance of symbols. We condemn ourselves continually out of our own mouths or buildings or sculpture or painting and other deeds. We cannot disregard their witness. If light is the final mystery, if John who waited in the desert could declare that God is light and that he was come to bear witness of that Light, and that it shineth in darkness though the darkness comprehended it not, should we not expect that while we do most faithfully reflect ourselves in many ways we will do so yet more truthfully in our treatment of light? What would a 'man from the moon' make of this, or simply an uncivilized visitor from some far country—the uncivilized man so often being more civilized than the civilized—what would he make of our cities of dreadful light? How could he fail to feel that here was a corrupt and degraded race?

Personally I know nothing that hurts so much as these

lights. There are the sins against soil, there are the sins against water, there are the sins against trees: they are more disastrous perhaps, but less vilifying than these sins against light. These lights, often hung from lamp-posts deliberately shaped like a gallows, are surely the most abominable of all thinkable corruptions. And it is really appalling how little rebellion there is against them, no one stones the ruffians who put them there. It is as if modern comforts and luxuries have robbed us of all religious feeling, of all æsthetic taste, and of all courage to trust our sensibilities, so that, the mere slaves of slaves, we meekly submit to the dictates of elected criminals and buffoons. Think of that vile symbol of recent times—the gas-mask. For what was it? It was not a mask— but *another face*. That low forehead, that loathsome chin, that disgraceful snout, did not make a mask but a face exactly congruous with the affair in hand. Yet men would look upon lines and lines of other men thus countenanced, without a qualm! We put on these things through fear of our own weapons. And we submit to these lights that dig deep trenches of corruption in every face—through fear of our motor-cars. A pretty pass!

CHAPTER TWO

Opening Windows

i

THE COMING OF GLASS

EVEN so we must retain perspective. Our excesses need not blind us to our successes. The reader might well be surprised if I were to conclude this part of my programme without mention of that manufacture which with light as its ally makes it possible for us to see through walls as if they did not exist, and in so many ways has given us civilization as we know it today. So I come to glass.

Glass is not a natural compound. Great heat turns sand into a liquid. When that liquid cools it becomes glass. Pure glass is an invisible stone, as it were. We cannot see it. It is not apparent, it is transparent we say. We see through it because the waves of light pass through it. It does not absorb all of them and give us a black stone. It does not reject all of them and give us a white stone. It does not select some of them and give us a coloured stone. The waves pass right through—quite easy, since everything is chiefly made of holes.

But we cannot speak of pure, clear glass as the kind which was made first. Glass has been manufactured for some five thousand years, but for many thousand years no one knew how to make uncoloured glass, something which you did not look *at* but *through*: you always saw through a glass darkly. Its history has been long and fruitful, from the

Egyptian beads to the twenty-ton block for the 200-inch telescope. We may note in passing that beads of glass have always exercised fascination, being especially appreciated by the untutored mind. 'When the white man first came to America,' write Rogers and Beard in their brilliant book, *Five Thousand Years of Glass*, 'he found the red man already occupying it and, strange to relate, the Indian entertained the impression that the land was his. If the white man wanted land he ought to pay for it.' The white man, who by the way was not yet 'an American', was deeply pained at this, not to say morally shocked. However, since the Indian was apparently unwilling to give up his inheritance without compensation the question arose as to whether there was anything he might be offered as a price for acres. Glass beads were tried. The Indians were delighted, thinking them a fair exchange for virgin soil. Since they were satisfied with glass beads why waste gold on them? A bead-mint was set up to the satisfaction of everyone—for a time.

It was not until the rise of that City whose inhabitants by paving their streets with water were to fill their pockets with gold and yet silence the roar of modernity, that glass came into its own to assume lovely shapes and blossom in abundance like flowers; and by the time that Venetian glass had become famous the secret of making it transparent had been discovered.

We still pause in wonder before a thin wall which we can see through. 'Windows are openings in the wall to admit light and air,' says the *Encyclopædia Britannica*. I had always thought that windows were light-openings in the wall by virtue of glass, thus admitting light but not rain, snow, or tigers. Yet of course the *E.B.* is right: windows did not primarily have glass and were simply openings, often being another description of the main-door. Sometimes you closed your window with wood or cloth; the idea of filling the space with glass came quite late, and ordinary house window-panes were such a luxury even in the America of 1829 that we learn that the Rev. Mr. Higginson of Salem advised all new-comers to bring their own panes with them. In Europe there were long periods when glass windows were not wanted at all. For ages the intermittent wars caused houses to take on the aspect of forts in which the windows were mere slits in the wall. However, eventually real window-panes began to come in until we reach modern times when some houses have whole sides made of them. In England it took some time before they assumed generous proportions, because between 1696 and 1851 the government pursued the good idea of taxing light and air. It grieved the more progressive business-men in the government to see such an excellent commodity as the sun being had for nothing. The difficulty was how to get people to pay for it. The problem was solved by a charge in terms of a window-tax. This policy met with sustained support for one hundred and thirty-five years from the best minds who considered that the fevers and plagues, which resulted from the insanitary conditions thus imposed, could scarcely be set against the advantages of the revenue received. A considerable number of cottages in Britain are still standing as a relic of those days. In the end, however, light was permitted to enter free of charge, and the abundant blessings of big glass windows have been enjoyed for a hundred years —which is as good a way as any of worshipping the sun and paying tribute to light.

ii

GLASS AND CIVILIZATION

The pure pane of glass through which light can easily pierce made possible the invention of our one happy prison. In a glass-house we can imprison heat. Having got in it cannot get out, and remains there for some time even when the sun has ceased to shine. My own appreciation of this is far from academic. I am aware how profitable it is for the growing of vegetables, fruit, and flowers; but I use one as a study and am able, on occasion, to sit down at a table in April when in actuality it is December or January. I have written about the sun scientifically in this book, but I have no desire to conceal the fact that I have always, and from a very early age, had a simple adoration of the sun as we know it in our part of the world. I cannot say with Wordsworth:

> . . . already I began
> To love the sun; a boy I loved the sun,
> Not as I since have loved him, as a pledge
> And surety of our earthly life, a light
> Which we behold and feel we are alive;
> Nor for his bounty to so many worlds—
> But for this cause, that I had seen him lay
> His beauty on the morning hills.

I cannot quite say that, for though I did see him lay his beauty on the Wicklow Mountains, I always loved the sun simply because it made me happy. The warmth without gave and gives me warmth within—even light within. To receive it in March or November from behind glass (with a cold wind outside) prompts me to draw up a list of things I could do without if I could have this thing. Why cannot the heat get out through the glass if it has got in? The answer is what we should expect: heat waves are a force, and the force is largely spent in getting in.

So many things followed the introduction of transparent glass that it has been fairly claimed that a list of them in terms of usefulness, knowledge, comfort, culture, and entertainment might serve as a description of modern civilization. Indeed this is so much the case that we have ceased to realize it. To take a single example, it scarcely occurs to us that the Romans never saw themselves in the mirror. The best that Cleopatra could make use of was a shiny surface. This was kind to the plain, but today we suffer from an excess of mirrors, forever being confronted with our faces. They have exercised a great fascination for people, and a history of mirrors would draw attention to the mirror-epidemics which have broken out in societies again and again. In the field of literature we got Alice. Sociologists even claim that it promoted biography. Thus Lewis Mumford makes the curious suggestion that 'The use of the mirror signalled the beginning of introspective biography in the modern style: that is, not as a means of edification but as a picture of the self, its depth, its mysteries, its inner dimensions.' Though he fails to support this with enough evidence, it is undoubtedly true that the bestowal of *depth* is one of the chief gifts of the mirror. We see deeper into reality, and discern more in the commonplace than before. This is partly due to the fact that the mirror is a *frame*. If we frame anything we see it, not only more clearly but with fresh vision; and this, I think, is why the framework of a novel is so important, for if that frame is good, then, in spite of a great deal of coincidence and unlikely re-meetings and so on, we get a greater concentration upon essential reality. Even when, standing back within a room, we look through a doorway or a window we see the section of the commonplace thus cut off, with new eyes. A mirror frames us back our own scene, somehow making it more mysterious and aloof and in a sphere of beauty[1] (note how the reflection in a motor-car's mirror, when going through an autumn-tinted tree-lined road, say, seems more significant than the 'straight' scene, however appealing). So fascinating is the mystery of mirrored reality, especially when presented the more elusively and remotely by water or copper, that Jacob Böhme declared that it was among the polished pots of his kitchen that he received intimation of the secret light of the Universe. We can scarcely hold it against Narcissus that he formed so favourable an impression of his mirrored image; and we may agree that the celebrated dog who preferred the reflection of his bone in the water to the bone itself, had the root of the matter in him.

Mirrors, though comparatively recent, are not modern any more than hot-houses. Nor are spectacles. In the thirteenth century Roger Bacon had already noted the properties of a dewdrop, how it acted as a lens bending the rays and magnifying or distorting the object. Lenses of glass were in use in the fifteenth century as eye-strengtheners, and at the end of it concave lenses came in by means of which the distorting lens of an imperfect eye was corrected by an opposite distortion (two wrongs thus making a right). This greatly added to the reading life, and with the invention of printing threw open those intellectual windows which we call the Revival of Learning. We enter modern times when the possibilities of the magnifying-glass became

---

[1] Note the mirror in Jan Van Eyck's famous 'Jan Arnolfini and his wife'. Thus in this picture the artist makes a double æsthetic assault.

fully realized. We know what the camera has meant to us—even allowing us, through means of the rays we call X, to photograph our insides and see how things are getting on there. Everyone has his own idea as to what the cinema is: personally I see it as a window through which we can look across to the farthest ends of the world.

iii

THE WINDOW OF THE TELESCOPE

There is no turning point in the alteration of man's perspective so complete as when in 1610 Galileo, after working night and day on his fifth telescope which made things thirty times nearer and a thousand times larger, viewed the heavens and announced what he saw in his *Siderius Nuncius*.

Today we brood upon the vastness of space. Before 1610 they saw just the same as we see when we regard the sky on a clear night without a telescope. But they did not conceive what we conceive. Evidently the prestige of the old cosmology was so great that all those stars worried them no more than if they were decorations upon a ceiling to the world. Then suddenly the idea of there being any kind of ceiling or even boundary was taken away and they were confronted with an infinite vastness. That was depressing enough. But the new findings went much further, not only refusing the assumed centrality of our earth but presupposing the existence of other earths such as our own. 'A new Philosophy arrests the Sunne,' declared Donne, 'And bids the passive earth about it runne.' That was bad: but Galileo's discovery of some new planets introducing the idea of a plurality of worlds was theologically unthinkable.

The powerful Church could not possibly allow it. Christ died for *this* world. A plurality would offer shocking obstacles to Faith. If God was to be conceived as the One and Only then He must be responsible for the creation of all the universe. If there were other worlds like ours in which He had placed imperfect beings in equal need of salvation, then—how could they be saved? The Church must instantly suppress such ideas. And just as Roger Bacon at an earlier date was thrown into prison for fourteen years because he insisted that the rainbow was not a special sign from heaven but a natural phenomenon, so Galileo must recant before the Inquisition, lest 'our whole beautiful system fall to the ground'. He did so, and spent the rest of his life a captive in his own house. His recantation was not thought strange at the time, but as the centuries passed his outrageous betrayal became such an unbearable blemish upon his name that future biographers invented his subsequent whisper after the denial: 'It is true all the same.'

However, since zealots have always been finally powerless against the majesty of truth the telescope itself could not be suppressed, and the sheer effect of its sense-perception, so much more powerful than any argument, shattered the old cosmology for ever. The homely conception of the universe was abandoned and men were compelled to contemplate the enormities of interstellar space. The Elizabethans had been perfectly happy with Aristotle and Ptolemy. The imagination of the greatest master of words the world has known was never stirred by Space. Time ruled Shakespeare like a king: in his day it was even more of a tyrant than in ours, for death knocked at the door so soon in those plagued and fevered times. The plays are riddled with Time and his sickle—but of Space there is nothing. And instead of astronomy just a little astrology in

King Lear. Then the heavens fell. Now it was open to some new great poet to grapple with the new conception. There was such a man. He had the imagination. He had the language. He had the art—even to encompass the illimitable. He did not do so. Instead he gave us the great ruin known as *Paradise Lost.* He gave us Genesis and the Garden of Eden in the very age that had opened up interstellar space. It was like building a cathedral to be bombed as soon as it was finished.

Milton thought he could have it both ways: the old story told against a background of the new cosmology. It would not work out. He could not afford even a minimum of scientific exactitude, and in any case the whole cast of his mind and educational upbringing was anti-scientific. But neither could he afford vagueness and evasion since these are the enemies of imagery. Heaven is up there somewhere; hell is down there somewhere; the earth is over there somewhere: perhaps that amount of vagueness would not have mattered any more than the creation of Light on the First Day and of the Sun on the Fourth Day as retold in Book VII, if the epic had been written in an earlier age. But Milton who was born in 1604 had been to Italy and had visited Galileo and looked through his telescope. That was naturally a tremendous experience. His imagination took wing. In Book II Satan leaves Hell to visit the Garden of Eden. He stands on the brink, 'Pondering his voyage; for no narrow frith he had to cross.' He found himself faced— *with the new cosmos.* It was terrible to contemplate. It was an illimitable waste without bound or dimension in which time and place were lost and where eldest night and chaos, ancestors of nature, hold eternal anarchy. It was a boiling and abortive gulf. It was a dark, unbottomed, and infinite abyss. It was an uncouth way, a vast abrupt, a profound void, a wide womb of uncreated and unessential night threatening the traveller with utter loss of being. Yet Satan takes the plunge. Soon he meets 'a vast vacuity' causing him to fall ten thousand fathoms in the wrong direction. He would be falling still, says Milton suddenly in the manner of a modern astronomer, 'and to this hour down had been falling', had he not 'by ill chance' met with 'a tumultuous cloud' which threw him in the right direction for Eden.

We need a universe which the kind of God depicted could create, we need a system offering the possibility of justifying the ways of God to man—that is we need definiteness and limitation. But it is definite and indefinite, it is limited and unboundaried and riddled with anomalies such as the presence of clouds where there could be no clouds, and air where there could be no air, and water where there could be no water, and even bogs where there could be no bogs, and on one occasion there is speculation as to how Satan could have shown Christ all the kingdoms of the world and the glory thereof without using a telescope.[1] Milton, whose mind moved with splendour in the field of classical allusion, did not consider that a blending of the natural with the unnatural and the physically ordinary with the impossible, mattered much so long as he got good effects; and when in Book VIII Adam remonstrates with Raphael on the grossly uneconomical manner in which the other stars administer to this one 'punctual spot', our little earth, he is told not to bother about it. This kind of thing does not trouble us when we read the poem in youth, for we surrender to its marvellous rhetoric and organ music; but later on we want the system to make sense, and if we do not go so far as Swift who implied that it would be just as sensible to hold that the universe is a large suit of clothes

[1] Actually this comes in *Paradise Regained*.

which invests everything, the earth by the air, the air by the stars, and the stars by the *primum mobile*, we are inclined to lay down this Epic and perhaps take up *The Prelude* which treats of 'this world which is the world of all of us, where we find our happiness or not at all'. *Paradise Lost* stands in literary history like some great Ruin on the plain, which not even in the past was ever inhabited, its great halls abandoned and bare, its glorious stained-glass windows long since shattered by the impious.

iv

THE WINDOW OF THE MICROSCOPE

When in the seventeenth century the windows were opened and Milton's generation heard 'a shout that tore Hell's concave, and beyond Frighted the reign of Chaos and old Night', it was not only sudden and unexpected but alarming, save for those strong souls who like Milton himself really exulted in the wild freedom of that frantic thought, and like Leibnitz beheld therein 'overflowing Benignity and Divine Super-abundance'. The world opened up by the microscope, which was in full use by about 1660, was less unexpected. With remarkable foreknowledge and exactitude of prophecy Francis Bacon had prepared men's minds in his *Novum Organum* for the secrets 'still laid up in the womb of nature' which would be revealed by new instruments in the years to come, and in *The New Atlantis* there are 'glasses and Meanes to see the small and Minute Bodies' and to inspect the structure 'of small insects and the flaws in Gemmes', though Bacon himself did not live to see his prophecy fulfilled.

The revelations of the microscope were in general received with wonder and joy. There are always some men temperamentally unable to face new prospects and who dwell perpetually in the shadow of the 'Night of the Soul'. Thus Pascal could not bear the new cosmology. 'The eternal silence of these infinite spaces frightens me,' he said. 'When I see the blindness and wretchedness of man,' he cried, 'when I regard the whole silent universe, and man without light, left to himself, and, as it were, lost in this corner of the universe, without knowing who has put him there, what he has come to do, what will become of him at death, and incapable of all knowledge, I become terrified, like a man who should be carried in his sleep to a dreadful desert island, and should awake without knowing where he is, and without means of escape. And thereupon I wonder how people in a condition so wretched do not fall into despair.' I would not for a moment question the ultimate profundity of those who grieve like this, nor deny 'the ineffaceable, sad birth-mark in the brow of man' as Melville read it, adding that 'the mortal man who hath more of joy than sorrow in him, that man cannot be true—not true, or undeveloped'. Yet at all times men have sought for signs and answers in the grass. In discerning the principle of beauty in all natural forms they have felt it as a promise and received it as a benediction. Not so with Pascal. Having surveyed the cosmic order he turned to 'the prodigy equally astonishing' revealed by the microscope. It also frightened him. The flea now seemed to him a fiend, 'its limbs with joints, veins in these limbs, blood in the veins, humours in this blood, globules in these humours, gases in these globules'. It was another abyss, 'the immensity of nature in the compass of this abbreviation of an atom'.

But this was far from being the general response to the

microscope when glass allied with light gave us eyes to pierce into the minutiæ of creation. It is true that its novelty sometimes alarmed simple people such as the inhabitants of a Tyrolese village who refused Christian burial to a certain man who had died with a fly in his pocket-lens, on the ground that he possessed on his person 'a devil shut up in glass'. But for the most part its revelations were hailed with gladness and were responsible for many a charming sentence from Leeuwenhock and Power, from Hooke and Browne and many others. They felt elation—as who does not?—when they traced the delicate fingers of design printed upon the tiniest envelopes of life. Henry Power marvelled to see on the butterfly 'the very Streaks of the Cœlestial pencil that drew them',[1] while the assistants of Leeuwenhock on drawing a flea and seeing 'the *little wheels* on the animals in *swift rotation*', continually cried out, 'O that one could ever depict so wonderful a motion!'[2] And just as to Sir Thomas Browne it seemed that 'in these narrow Engines there is more curious Mathematicks; and the Civility of these little Citizens more neatly sets forth the Wisdom of their Maker'[3] than is to be discerned in the motions of an eagle, so also Robert Hooke when gazing upon the seeds of thyme and noticing how well they are protected from outward dangers, observes in language as felicitous as the illustrations to his wonderful *Micrographia* that Nature 'as if she would from the ornaments wherewith she hath deckt these Cabinets, hint to us that in them she has laid up her Jewels and Masterpieces' and that 'the Creator may in these characters have written and engraved many of His most mysterious designs and Counsels'.

[1] *Experimental Philosophy* (1663).
[2] Marjorie Nicolson: *The Microscope and English Imagination.*
[3] *Religio Medici.*

This discovery of the minute preceded by at least a century the discovery of wild nature in mountains and waterfalls as means to experience the divine. Indeed Henry Baker suggested that it were better to look at a mite than at an elephant, while Robert Boyle thought that 'wonder dwells not so much on Nature's Clocks than on her Watches'; and it was not only Blake who beheld the universe in a grain of sand but Traherne who declared that 'you never enjoy the world aright till you see how a sand exhibiteth the wisdom and power of God'.[1] This was a new attitude. Generally speaking, in the seventeenth century before the arrival of the microscope Nature was thought of as ragged and uncouth over against Art which was so elegant and finished. With the coming of the microscope the tables were turned: it was Art which seemed rude and Nature that was polished. Thus when Henry Baker looked at artefacts through the microscope he discerned only a concealment of deformity and an imposition upon our want of sight, whereas he claimed that in Nature the more we look at the least and meanest of her productions, flea or fly or louse or mite, nothing can be found but beauty and perfection; and when he examined the particles of matter composing salts and saline substances set at liberty by dissolution and beheld the order in terms of rhombs, pyramids, pentagons, hexagons, and octagons in mathematical exactitude, 'moving in Rank and File obedient to unalterable laws in determined figures', he saw 'Almighty Wisdom and Power'.[2] John Wilkins declared that 'whatever is Natural doth by that appear adorned with all imaginable Elegance and Beauty', as against the 'rude bungling and deformed work' of men, so that the finest needle seems but

[1] *Centuries of Meditations*, No. 27.
[2] *The Microscope Made Easy.*

blunt when compared with 'the inimitable Gildings and Embroideries in the smallest Seeds or Head and Eye of a fly' such as issue from 'Nature's forge and furnace',[1] while to George Adams the Younger (the Elder wrote in the same strain) the contrast was humiliating, and when he saw closely the many fibres of a flower he was enchanted, adding that 'the whole substance presents a celestial radiance in its colouring, with a richness superior to silver or gold, as if it were intended for the Cloathing of an Angel'.[2] Yet perhaps the strongest impression made was that of an endless fund of life to be discovered everywhere. Addison's tiny dream-visitor in the world of the microscope beheld 'millions of species' on a green leaf, and became lost in a forest of trees growing in the cup of an acorn;[3] while there is a curious up-to-dateness in the declaration of Fontenelle that 'solid Bodies are nothing but an immense swarm of imperceptible Animals' and that 'everything is animated, and the stones upon Salisbury Plain are as much alive as a hive of bees'.[4]

Even so it was not the delight of the poets, nor the conclusions of the philosophers, nor the amusement of the satirists, from Swift with his Gulliver and his famous quatrain on the flea to those who made play with the 'philosophic girls' who preferred microscopes to lovers, which made this instrument so important in laying the foundations of modern civilization. It was its effect on medicine. In 1674, Antony van Leeuwenhock when passing a lake decided to take a pail of water from it and examine it through his microscope. He saw creatures a thousand times

[1] *The Principles and Duties of Natural Religion.*
[2] *Essays on the Microscope.*
[3] *Tatler*, No. 119, Jan. 12, 1709.
[4] *A Plurality of Worlds*, pp. 89–90.

smaller than the smallest ones he had seen upon the rind of
cheese or in wheaten flour or mould. Then, as he told the
Royal Society in his Letters, he sampled a pail of rain-water
and found creatures 'more than ten thousand times smaller
than the ordinary animalcules'. He was delighted with the
perfection of these tiny creatures also; he felt abashed before
the Creator to behold structures 'so delightsome and
wondrous'; the whole water seemed 'to be alive with these
multifarious animalcules. This was for me, among all the
marvels that I have discovered in Nature, the most marvellous of all.' He had discovered bacteria and protozoa. He
had opened the door of microbiology and bacteriology. He
had thus laid the foundations for the observation of the
circulation of the blood. He had paved the way for the
introduction of all the antitoxins which rescue us from so
many plagues and fevers. He was responsible for the final
marvels of Fleming's penicillin no less than for the inocu-
lations of Pasteur.

Still, I am unwilling to close my account of glass and
light on this note. I have kept for the last our happiest
victory in this kind. It is entirely æsthetic and spiritual. It is
not the transparent variety I have in mind, but stained-
glass. Man has never guided light to better purpose than
with the stained-glass window in church or cathedral. A
beautiful specimen of this art in a place of worship, not over-
lighted by plain windows, works upon us. It may be a
cathedral in the great city; better still, a small church en-
folded in the English hills, sequestered and hung with
history. At any time we can enter into the seclusion of the
holy place, and wrapped in the solitude that is not loneliness
gaze up at the window where light turned to colour receives
light again; and if the beams of the setting sun fall upon it

so that the colour of the rays works with the colour in the waves—a double effect, a multiplied miracle—then truly physics joins with metaphysics, and the sombre radiance of that melancholy light belongs to the kingdom of heaven.

CHAPTER THREE

Sun-Worship

i

SUN-GODS

As I passed along a country lane recently on a winter late afternoon I turned a corner to find that a big red ball had got stuck in the twigged network of a hawthorn tree. It was too large for children to play with if I took it down, but might serve. I did not find it really natural to accept the fact that it was not in the tree but over ninety million miles away.

Sometimes a simple little experience of that sort gets us closer to the mystery of things than our present extensive intellectual knowledge. Today we know a great deal about the unity of, and our own unity with natural phenomena—but we do not feel it. Our ancestors felt it—though they did not know much about it.

It is really a pleasure for us to contemplate the cosmology of earlier men. In modern times we interpret the heavens not as the eye sees it but as the mind knows it. As their eyes saw it so their minds conceived it. Over their heads was the blue, white-scarfed roof of the world at night tastefully hung with lanterns, the moon a radiant face about ten miles off, while above the roof lay heaven, where you went after death and had a good time. It was not too difficult to feel at home, even if fearful, in such a universe. The sun was no lonely, lofty castaway millions of miles off, but a Being who would be

122

glad to be offered a drink to quench his thirst as he completed his exhausting journey across the sky. He was a god: and a god in early days was always regarded as remarkably human. Thus Phœbus Apollo, the most famous of all sun-gods, was so clearly conceived in personal terms by his devotees that they thought him to be jealous enough to cause the ears of King Midas to lengthen till they resembled those of an ass, and had Marsyas flayed alive for saying that he played the flute better than himself; and later, when Anaxagoras not only denied the idea of the sun's divinity, the idea of its personality, and even the idea that it was a Universal Eye which beheld everything, and declared that it was merely a mass of hot iron about the size of the Peloponnesus, he met with the greatest indignation and escaped death only through the intervention of Pericles. The Cherokee Indians thought that the sun hated the people of the earth because they never looked straight at her without screwing up their faces—'My grandchildren', she is represented as saying, 'are ugly; they grin all over their faces when they look at me, but for the Moon they smile.'

Those who could watch the sun daily rising from the sea took it as a white bull, and for thousands of years the Kings of Egypt delighted to style themselves Ra, the mighty bull; while the phenomenon of it sinking into the sea made them think that it was swallowed by a monster who in the morning disgorged its prey into the Eastern sky—a myth said to be responsible later on for the story of Jonah and even of Little Red Riding Hood. It is not surprising to learn that in some quarters the people, expecting it to make a hissing noise as it sank into the water, claimed, in the manner of eye-witnesses and ear-witnesses the world over in all ages, that they did actually hear that sound. The Ægean Islanders believed that every evening the sun returned to his kingdom in the underworld where his mother waited for him with forty loaves. If they were not ready he would eat his entire family. On rising red from the sea the islanders said: 'He has eaten his mother.'

When we survey the sun-legends of early man and wish to understand them, we must be careful not to think in our own consequent terms. It was quite possible to put out the sun if you wanted to make mischief, like that poor Indian boy who finding people uncharitable to him threatened to shoot the sun, and did so, and the light went out at once, and the whole world became dark. It was not always assumed that you could have a sun unless you took the trouble to get one: thus Coyate-Man is represented as going on a journey and finding a land flowing with sunshine. He offers to buy it, but they will not sell. So he resolves to steal it, and does so, though it was carefully guarded by a turtle. The Apache myth held that when their ancestors wanted a better system of lighting they simply devised a sun, while the North Americans believed that either a wolf or a raven or a hawk had procured one for them. It could perform simple tasks for you: since it is obviously the sun who sends down hailstones, it could easily send you a new tooth. Thus an Arab boy, on his tooth falling out, would take it between finger and thumb and throw it towards the sun saying: 'Give me a better one for it.' The sun is seen to travel backwards and forwards, so why should it not give one's absent husband a lift home on the return journey, complying in compassion to the plaint: 'May the grief that my absence causes him make him weep, may the grief that my absence causes him make him lament, may the grief that my absence causes him make him break the obstacles that part us and bring him back to me at sunrise.'[1]

[1] J. G. Frazer: *The Magic Art*, I. p. 166.

ii

THE SUN AS SAVIOUR

Where we would say that the sun is rising high in the heavens, they said: 'The sun has harnessed the horses for his journey.' Swift horses were associated in the solar mythology of the Indians, the Persians, the Hebrews, and the Greeks. Sometimes it was given wings and thought of as a bird—'The bird of day is weary and has fallen into the sea.' The North Americans saw it as a hare. The Greeks wove the most charming fancies around the expedition. Seeing in the flashing rays spirited and fiery steeds harnessed with gleaming trappings and burnished reins they annually dedicated to him a carriage and four horses, and flung them into the sea for his use, since his old ones would be worn out. It was sometimes considered that he went too fast, and wishing to retard his progress certain races used a net to catch him, or summoned a strong man to imprison him in a tower, or in the manner of Joshua frankly commanded him to stand still. Indeed, they were far from thinking of the sun always as a very powerful god. To many it seemed strange that he should mount the sky each morning with absolute regularity and pursue the same path. They thought he must be compelled to do so. Once he may have done what he liked until caught in a trap and beaten into submission, bound with cords, held fast by eight hundred thousand gods who have ever since retained him. The Inca of Peru denied the sun's deity as supreme, on the ground that his course was so circumscribed. 'If he were free,' he declared, 'he would visit other parts of the heavens where he had never been; but as he follows one path he must be tied like a beast.'

Yet the most pleasing legends spring from the conception of the sun as saviour and servant of mankind. It has
a task which it must perform. It has a path to travel from
which it must not deviate. It has ever before it a life of toil
from which it cannot swerve. Thus the heroic figure of
Hercules, still our symbol for the greatest deeds of endurance and strength, was shaped by the imagination of mankind. 'Nowhere', says Cox, 'is the unutterable toil and
scanty reward of the sun brought out so prominently as in
the whole legend, or rather in the mass of unconnected
legends which is gathered round the person of Herakles.'
Interpreted in any other light his adventures are rather
tiresome but considered 'as the luminary that gives light
to the world, as the god who impregnates all nature with
his fertilizing rays, every part of the legend teems with
animation and beauty, and is marked by a pleasing and
perfect harmony'.[1] In a more simple form the figure of
Sisyphus who was condemned to spend his days laboriously
rolling a great stone to the top of a hill, after which it
rolled down again, signifies the solar sphere gradually
mounting its zenith each day, only to slip down again. We
must add the agonies of Ixion and the tortures of Tantalus,
the one bound for life to a four-spoked ever-revolving
wheel, the other with his head above water, dying of thirst
yet tantalizingly unable to drink, as further examples of
solar symbolism.

Since primitive man always strove to interpret natural
things in terms of the familiar language of daily existence
and to attribute a human agency to manifestations of
physical laws, the part which night and darkness played in
the making of myths was necessarily very great. 'In the
thought of these early ages,' says Cox again, 'the sun was

[1] Anthon's *Classical Dictionary*.

the child of night and darkness, the dawn came before he was born, and died as he rose in the heavens. He strangled the serpents of the night, he went forth like a bridegroom out of his chamber and like a giant to run his course. He had to do battle with clouds and storms, sometimes his light grew dim under their gloomy veil and the children of men shuddered at the wrath of the hidden sun. His course might be brilliant and beneficent, or gloomy, sullen, and capricious. He might be a warrior, a friend, or a destroyer. The rays of the sun were changed into golden hair, into spears and lances and robes of light.'

In the night another luminary appeared, the moon, and it was natural that the sun should be conceived as pursuing the moon across the sky, the coy moon for ever flying, yet the pair meeting in matrimonial embrace in the interval between the old and new moon; and this was thought to be a good time for human marriages, for on the principle of sympathetic magic when the sun was wedded in the sky men and women should be wedded on earth. Some thought of the sun and moon as brother and sister or husband and wife from the beginning, and the stars as their children. Other legends suggested that the moon agreed to eat her children for the benefit of mankind who could not bear so much heat and brightness, and that the sun devours her children at dawn. It seemed also that the sun often bit the moon, either angrily or amorously, taking a neat curved slice out of it as from a cake, occasionally leaving only a very small piece. One legend tells how the Sun, the Moon, and Pole Star were all suitors for the hand of a beautiful maiden hatched from a goose's egg. The girl objected to the Moon as unstable, with a face which sometimes narrowed in an unpleasant manner, and with a bad habit of roving about all night and remaining idle at home all day. She did not regard the Sun with much more favour since he was the cause of too much heat in summer, cold in winter, and uncertain weather conditions. She chose the Pole Star who always came home punctually.

The Norse myths display just as many sun-heroes who accomplish impossible tasks and vanquish formidable foes. The sun is Odin's eye, Balder's countenance, Heimdal's need—'And still she rides, the beaming maid, from morn to night.' In the Finnish legends we find the sun as a lamp illuminating the halls of Vanna Issa, the Supreme Deity, and entrusted by him to the care of two immortal servants, a youth and a maiden—Dawn and Evening Twilight. Thus, in the words of this charming creed, the Father says: 'Unto thee my daughter I entrust the Sun. Extinguish him and hide him lest he come to harm. And unto thee my son I entrust the duty to rekindle him for a new course. On no day must the light be absent from the arch of heaven.' There is melancholy as well as poetry in the touchingly personal tale. 'In the winter he resteth a great while, but in summer his repose is short, and Evening Twilight gives up the dying light into the very hands of Dawn who straightway kindles it into new life. At such times they each take one look deep into the other's dark brown eyes; they press each other's hands, and their lips touch. Once a year only for the space of four weeks they come together at midnight. The Evening Twilight layeth the dying light into the hands of Dawn, and the cheeks of Evening Twilight redden, and the rosy redness is mirrored in the sky till Dawn rekindles the light.'[1]

---

[1] W. T. Olcott: *Sun Lore in All Ages.*

iii

SOLAR RELICS

'In the childhood of mankind,' says Paley, 'the daily death of the sun was regarded as a reality.' It is a little difficult to credit this, seeing that it happened every twenty-four hours. But it is clear enough that its efforts were a constant topic of anxiety, and it is certain that once a year it alarmed them terribly: it began to fail in autumn and to fall into increasing depression as winter drew on. Older than all history and all written records has been the fear that took hold of the people at this decay of their god of light and warmth. Was he dying, or would he revive and reappear?—that was the awful question. There were no almanacs, no calendars, no systematic ordering of time into seasons and years, no memory about what happened last year—all they knew was that their chief source of comfort and life was failing. What was happening during the short days which we know as the end of the year? The god had fallen upon evil times. He had come under the malign influence of the Serpent and the Scorpion. Delilah, the queen of night, had shorn his hair (Samson is derived from *Shemesh*, the sun); Typhon, the prince of darkness had betrayed him; the dreadful Boar had wounded him; Herakles was perhaps himself being slain at last. Would he grow weaker and weaker and finally succumb? 'We can imagine the anxiety with which those early men and women watched for the first indication of a lengthening day; and the universal joy when the Priest (the representative of primitive science) having made some simple observations, announced from the Temple steps that the day *was* lengthening—that the Sun was really born again to a new and glorious career.'[1] That would have been roughly on December 25th.

The time came at last when natural phenomena were no longer deified, and one invisible god took the place of the many visible ones. But numerous festivals and rites of solar origin are with us still, entwined into the fabric of modern civilization. The Roman festival of the winter solstice, celebrated on December 25th in honour of the sun-god Mithra, known as the 'Birthday of the Unconquered Sun' was introduced into the Christian Church in the fourth century as a festival in honour of the birth of Jesus Christ. Augustus and Gregory drew the people's attention to 'the glowing light and dwindling darkness that follow the Nativity', while Leo the Great denounced the idea that Christmas Day is to be honoured not for the birth of Christ but for the rising of the sun. But the old paganism died hard and the Christian teachers found it unwise to attempt a complete break with cherished practices. Sun-worship lies at the heart of great Christian festivals, the heathen relics blending with beliefs antagonistic to the spirit that prompted them, and nothing proves more clearly the appeal of solar idolatry than the efforts made by Moses to prohibit it. 'Take care,' he cried to the Israelites, 'lest when you lift your eyes to Heaven and see the sun, the moon, and all the stars, you be seduced!' When today we light our candles on our Christmas trees it is but a remnant of the rite which was to guide the sun-god back to life; and when we eat our plum-pudding we realize that though it is an act grossly incongruous with the sorrow and suffering of Jesus, it is in harmony with a feast in honour of the sun as held in ancient times when cakes of corn and fruit were laid on

[1] Edward Carpenter: *Pagan and Christian Creeds.*

130

altars dedicated to the Lord of Light. And as a matter of fact most Christian peoples to this day prefer to celebrate Christmas frankly in the manner of a pagan festival.

Since the sun rises in the East, that came to be considered the most propitious direction to face on ritualistic occasions, and the word Easter is as clearly related to sun-movements as the word East, while in China there was a popular belief that if only the Emperor would steadfastly turn his countenance towards the East there would be perfect harmony on earth. In Europe we face the East when reciting the Creed, in Mexico when kneeling in prayer, and a certain Baptismal rite ensured that he who embraced the Faith first turned towards the West and renounced Satan with gestures of abhorrence. We know how the architects of St. Peter's in Rome so exactly placed the Basilica due East and West that on the vernal equinox the great doors could be thrown open at sunrise and the rays thus penetrate through the nave and illuminate the High Altar, just as in pagan days the granite blocks were so arranged at Stonehenge that at the summer solstice the shadow of one stone fell exactly on the stone in the centre of the circle, indicating to the priests that the new year had begun and the signal could be given for flashing the news through the land.

We find solar significance in words and actions unrecognized as such by the conscious mind. Thus the most ancient symbol of the sun is a wheel with spokes for rays, and if we dig into the derivation we find that our word wheel comes from Yole or Yuul, Hiaul or Huul, meaning Sun and used as a festival term at the winter solstice, so that we still speak of the Yule Log. We find relics of sun-worship in many of our most familiar signs. It was the custom of painters when representing the head of Christ, or the Virgin, or even that of some particularly saint-like person, to place upon it the solar circle or disc, while we still speak of a man as 'being worthy of a halo'. The simple cross with perpendicular and transverse arms of equal length representing the spokes of the solar wheel sending out rays in all directions found upon the monuments and utensils of every primitive people, evolved into the symbol of the Cross which because of its sadness and poignancy held an immense appeal for suffering mankind, and came at last to stand for the price of redemption through the Christian scheme of salvation; and we all know well enough how in 1939, on account of the Christian tendency toward forgiveness, meekness, and appeasement, that other emblem of the vernal sun, the Swastika, signifying vitality, health, violence, ruthlessness, power, and glory, was raised against the Cross in mortal combat by Hitler's heathen hordes.

iv

THE SCIENTIFIC APPROACH

When we think of our modern sun-temples we might well bear in mind the Egyptian solar religion. Astonished by the sublime order of the universe they exalted the sun as the central object in significance, naming it Osiris, also called Ra, with its eternal and primary companion Isis, the moon, and set up great temples such as that of Amen-Ra, at Karnak, 'One of the most soul-inspiring temples which have ever been conceived or built by man,' says Sir Norman Lockyer. Covering twice the area of St. Peter's, its vastness is unchallenged in the ecclesiastical world; straight and true its stone avenue runs for five hundred yards, thus limiting the light into one narrow beam carried to the other extremity of the building into the sanctuary to illuminate at the solstice the image of Ra.

Our sun-temple is an observatory. Our belief, far out-stripping our belief in Scripture, is in Science. We are inclined to think that the Egyptian shrine only expressed ignorance of the true nature of the sun which is not a god but a ball of fire ninety-three million miles off. Yet we might fairly put it another way. They were under an illusion with regard to the natural facts about the sun, but their Knowledge, which with a capital K may be taken as implying awareness of the total significance concerning phenomena, was not inferior to ours. We know the facts. We know a tremendous amount of facts. They take the place of significance in our minds. Think of that most modern of all productions, the *Encyclopædia Britannica*. Think of its weight upon the intellect, and of its deliberate, its planned refusal to contain a single sentence set down with the purpose of exciting total awareness, as if that part of man's mind, the imagination, is worth nothing. Think of the encouragement given nowadays to millions through crossword and quiz to suppose that their bits and pieces of information constitute knowledge; and imagine the consternation and scandal on the faces of quiz-master and quizzee, if, on a single occasion it were suggested that the prize should be handed to the man who had smartly answered questions on mythology, only on condition that he could give an intelligent answer as to the significance and meaning of myth!

Is there much point in classifying everything and being aware of nothing? Yes; on that basis we can do a great deal. Once in possession of this factual knowledge about phenomena we can build up our civilization with its advantages and comforts. That is something—even if we endanger it all with that bomb we dislike so much and make so eagerly.

But we cannot expect to have much in the way of religion (as apart from theologies). And of course we can be just as credulous as our ancestors, in the modern manner, ready to take as gospel the scriptures of science, and to accept without batting an eyelid, for instance, the announcement that the solar system is merely one 'island' amongst millions in space travelling from nowhere to nowhere at a thousand miles a second (quite possibly true). There is little to choose between on the one hand the Aristotelians who insisted that the findings of Galileo, Scheiner, and Fabricius concerning the spots on the sun were a delusion and that it was out of keeping with the dignity of the Eye of the Universe to suppose that it could be inflicted with so plebeian a complaint as ophthalmia, and on the other hand the Rev. Tobias Snowden who commanded a considerable following in the nineteenth century when he published a book proving the sun to be Hell and the dark spots gatherings of damned souls; while we ourselves swallow with little demur the ruling of the experts who relate the periodicity of sun-spots and turbulence with affairs on earth such as the migration of swallows, the yield of harvests, and the revolutions of states. Unfortunately our modern credulity is not accompanied by any sense of the *numinous*, of what used to be called 'participation', of reverence, of that 'experience of awe before the pure phenomena' which Goethe considered to be the highest faculty in man.

There is nothing abstruse or even fresh in these remarks. We are accustomed to hear them made. 'A lot of people think that a little peasant boy of the present day who goes to a primary school knows more than Pythagoras did, simply because he can repeat, parrot-wise, that the earth moves round the sun,' said Simone Weil in *The Need for Roots*; and adds: 'In actual fact he no longer looks up at the heavens.

The sun about which they talk to him in class hasn't, for him, the slightest connexion with the one he can see. He is severed from the universe surrounding him.' But I cannot agree that such severance is a prerequisite of modern knowledge. There is no inevitable dichotomy between the scientific and the religious approach—for myself, I feel no such 'split'. There is no reason why the facts which great and devoted men lay before us should be regarded as alien to the soul, or as 'mere facts' useful only for practical purposes or for passing examinations. They can equally well feed the imagination. The split is not real; but to suppose its existence has been easier since the coming of Newton.

CHAPTER FOUR

Science and Imagination

i

NEWTON AND THE POETS

ON 28 December 1817, Wordsworth, Keats, Lamb, and Benjamin Haydon dined together. They discussed the merits of Homer, Shakespeare, Milton, and Virgil. As the evening advanced Lamb became slightly the better for drink, and as a set-off to the solemnity of Wordsworth he abused Haydon for putting Newton's head into a picture he had just finished—'a fellow who believed nothing unless it was as clear as three sides of a triangle'. Then he and Keats agreed that Newton had destroyed all the poetry of the rainbow by reducing it to its prismatic colours. They all ended with a toast, 'drinking Newton's health and confusion to mathematics'.[1]

I'm not quite sure why they drank Newton's health under the circumstances, but let that pass. Though in their cups— and perhaps maudlin—their tone was true to the general feeling that science was no longer on the side of poetry, nay, that it was the enemy of creative imagination. Today no one would be surprised at such an attitude, but it was not always so. In the Middle Ages the 'sciences' were 'the arts of the mind'. Every branch of learning was a *scientia*, and whether the subject was grammar, logic, geometry, music, or other things, the term 'sciences' or 'arts' could be used.

[1] *The Autobiography and Memoirs of Benjamin Haydon.*

136

We still pay letter-tribute to the sense of this. I myself am a Bachelor of Arts. When I got it I was considered as having achieved a degree—of what? In what lay this degree of excellence? I could not have claimed it in Art, still less in Science. But the implications are sound and pleasant, however unworthy the recipient, and remind us of the old days when 'science was used to define knowledge generally, the state or fact of knowing,' as Sir Ifor Evans puts it, 'while Philosophy was still widely used to define Science as we now understand it.'[1] In fact 'a philosophical apparatus' meant a scientific apparatus.

When in the sixteenth century Sir Philip Sidney spoke of a tale which holdeth children from play and old men from the chimney corner, it was not of stories he was thinking, but of knowledge. In the seventeenth century there was little or no conflict between science and literature. Science nourished the works of Sir Thomas Browne; Robert Hooke's *Micrographia* is a real work of art; and perhaps my brief quotations in the previous chapter from Baker and Wilkins and Adams and even Leeuwenhock will suggest that even those who had no pretensions as literary men yet wrote with considerable felicity under the inspiration of the simple science of the day. Richard Baxter, Jeremy Taylor, and Joseph Glanville all approached science with pleasure and without misgiving. It was possible for a man such as Samuel Pepys to be President of the Royal Society; Dryden, Waller, and Denham were happy to associate themselves with it; and Abraham Cowley, who was among the first to be nominated for the Society, had great influence and significance in his day.

Newton was a seventeenth-century, early eighteenth-century man (1642–1727). His *Principia* was written in

[1] See his valuable *Literature and Science.*

Latin and was in any case beyond the understanding of literary men, but his *Optics* was understood, and at first it attracted the writers of the day. In fact the minor poets composed pieces in his praise, the best known being James Thomson's 'Ode to the Memory of Sir Isaac Newton',[1] elaborately eulogizing his theory of light. Newton gave Pope material for poetry and Swift material for satire. Pope was so great an artist that almost anything he had to say reads as well now as two hundred years ago. Indeed some of his lines gather force year by year, perhaps the most pertinent example appearing in Book II in the *Essay on Man*:

> Go, wondrous creature! mount where Science guides
> Go, measure earth, weigh air, and state the tides,
> Instruct the planets in what orbs to run,
> Correct old Time, and regulate the sun;
> Go teach Eternal Wisdom how to rule—
> Then drop into thyself, and be a fool.

This is criticism of man and not a reaction against science. The point and strength of the *Essay* lies in the fact that the muse, so far from being weakened by science, acquires material to work on, even if in terms of criticism. The same might be said of Donne over a century earlier. His famous lines:

> And new Philosophy calls all in doubt
> The Element of fire is quite put out;
> The Sun is lost, and th' earth and no man's wit
> Can well direct him where to look for it. . . .

are often quoted as being written by a man who felt that

[1] Marjorie Nicolson: *Newton Demands the Muse.*

the new learning introduced with Galileo had thrown men into confusion. But it may be questioned whether Donne was really very perturbed. He was an exceedingly clever man, and I suspect he enjoyed the opportunity for epigram and was glad to use science to fertilize his rhyme. It was the same with Swift (1667–1745). It was all grist to his mill. Being no respecter of persons he did not respect Newton (as Pope did) nor trouble to understand him. He simply had his fun, especially in 'The Voyage to Laputa' in *Gulliver's Travels*. Pope wears much better than Swift. In spite of his celebrated prose-style Swift is, for the most part, tedious now: he seems off the point as far as we are concerned.

ii

BLAKE AND WORDSWORTH

After Newton had been dead for thirty years William Blake was born (1757–1827) who declared war upon him for twenty years; after he had been dead for twenty-two years Goethe was born (1749–1832) who declared war upon him for thirty years. The two poets have nothing in common save this enmity to Newton—and I must let Goethe stand down for the moment. Blake was the first great poet to propose manifestoes against science; he was the first to get hold of a knife and cut people's heads up. He made a tremendous slash through the skull neatly dividing the cranium into two equal parts. In one half he discovered vision, imagination, intuition; in the other half he discovered reason, analysis, and the desire for experiment: one was spiritual, the other materialist; one was right, the other wrong; one was good, the other bad. The way of analysis was the way of corruption and mockery, the words 'reason' and 'experiment' were the slogans of the devil; and this was the way of Descartes and of Locke, and these were the slogans of Bacon and Newton.

> Mock on, Mock on Voltaire, Rousseau:
> Mock on, Mock on: 'tis all in vain!
> You throw the sand against the wind,
> And the wind blows it back again.
>
> And every sand becomes a Gem
> Reflected in the beams divine;
> Blown back they blind the mocking Eye,
> But still in Israel's path they shine.
>
> The Atoms of Democritas
> And Newton's particles of Light
> Are sands upon the Red Sea shore,
> Where Israel's tents do shine so bright.

The poem is slightly obscure (in the right way of being obscure) but we would not have it otherwise. Blake's particular kind of inspiration, his God-intoxication, his immediacy of response could not be nourished by science and might very well be injured by analysis so that a grain of sand would cease to be a gem reflected in the beams divine. When he looked at the setting sun he didn't see 'a little round disc about the size of a shilling. Oh no, I see a company of the Heavenly Host crying—Holy, holy, holy Lord God Almighty!' We do not take him literally but it is clear that his inspiration was of that order which could not be supported by the scientific approach. It is also clear that he was upset by the theory of primary and secondary qualities elaborated by Descartes and Locke. Blake was one of the most glorious poets who ever existed, and I am unwilling to bother about his polemics. He was easily enraged. Even Wordsworth's pantheism gave him a severe stomach complaint.

The position of Wordsworth in this matter is ironical. It is true that his famous lines on Newton 'with his prism and silent face, The marble index of a mind for ever Voyaging through strange seas of Thought, alone' are never forgotten (who could forget them?) but it seems that he is firmly fixed as having declared that it was murder to dissect, and that a scientist is the man who would peep and botanize upon his mother's grave; though if we examine the context of the latter remark we find that he was simply making a plea for regarding individuals as individuals and not as types in the sociological Sidney Webb manner, while surely any poet, conscious of his intense experience of beauty, may be allowed to mutter the words, 'We murder to dissect,' faced with moralists and analysts pure and simple. Less well known are the following words from his introduction to *The Lyrical Ballads*: he looks to the time when 'the remotest discoveries of the Chemist, the Botanist, or Mineralogist will be as proper objects of the Poet's art as any upon which it can be employed. If the time should ever come when what is now called Science, thus familiarized to men shall be ready to put on, as it were, a form of flesh and blood, the Poet will lend his divine spirit to aid the transfiguration.' Those words might well be used today as the apologia or manifesto of those who believe that the time has now come for the poet to exhibit before the public gaze the spoils and trophies of the investigators.

But that does not complete the irony of Wordsworth's position. It happens that he is the poetic pet lamb chosen

by scientists who are anxious to show how the poets support
their theories. The best example of this may be found in
Whitehead's chapter on 'The Romantic Reaction' in his
Science and the Modern World. He quotes one of Wordsworth's
famous apostrophes to Nature in *The Prelude* with approval
as 'exhibiting entwined prehensive unities, each suffused
with model presences of others'. Indeed it may be so. But
had that been the main point of the poem Wordsworth
might just as well have written in prose. The point lay in
the experience of joy which this consciousness brought
with it. It may please Whitehead that Wordsworth lent
support to his theory of prehensive unification and even of
misplaced concreteness, but neither Wordsworth nor any
other poet minds very much whether or not his exalted
experience is supported by the theories of science. I do not
deny the intellectual satisfaction which this synthesis undoubtedly affords. It gives pleasure to many people. I often
hear people say: 'Things are looking up! The scientists
have abandoned their old theories of matter and are now
declaring that it is vanishing before their eyes.' They are
pleased when they say this. Their eyes sparkle. They smile.
But what are they actually saying? Only that what was hard
is now soft. That what seemed to be a solid slab is really a
whirling mass of electric particles. They think that this
makes matter less material and more spiritual. They equate
electricity with spirit. Thus the more electricity we have
the more spirit we have. I am not sure where this leads us.
If it is true it will be of little concern whether we call ourselves materialists or idealists. Of course it may be true.
Many good men have derived satisfaction from this thought.
'Spirit is matter seen in a stronger light,' suggests L. P. Jacks
with emphasis, and adds that when the late Sir William
Bragg, President of the Royal Society, maintained that

'light is the basis of matter and the substance of the Whole', he was giving 'another wording for Spinoza's Substance'.[1] It is more than likely. All I am saying is that we are at an advantage if we experience these things—as did Spinoza— rather than only reason about their possibility. A drop of truly experienced harmony is worth an ocean of intellectual synthesis. Experience is a bigger gun than theory in this sphere, and just as the man with strong religious intimations is not in the least parasitic upon the validity of any historic event, so the poet in his exultation is entirely independent of any scientific theory. Dependence here upon the changing scientific approaches leads to confusion. It is deplorable to see learned men of strong minds—if they really are strong —plucking metaphysical comfort from the Quantum Theory on the ground that it suggests that Nature is rather less a determined system than we had thought—a conclusion which seems to me as absurd as the comfort. I am relieved to find that I am not singular in maintaining this view. 'While I think that the argument which finds evidence for human free-will in the supposed discovery of indeterminacy in Nature is entirely groundless,' writes Professor Herbert Dingle, 'I think that the nineteenth-century argument against human free-will because of the supposed deter-minacy in Nature is equally groundless. Our consciousness of freedom is an immediate experience, and as such is a fundamental datum. It is inconceivable that experience can be refuted by deductions from experience.'[2] That observa-tion might fruitfully be contrasted with the long speech in Shaw's *Too True To Be Good* delivered by the distracted Elder through whom the great playwright so faithfully mirrored the confusion of our time.

[1] 'They Do Ill Who Leave This Out' in *Near the Brink*.
[2] 'The New Outlook in Physics' in *The Scientific Adventure*.

iii

KEATS AND THE RAINBOW

This brings me back to Keats and the rainbow. It may seem a little strange that the man who claimed that the experience of Beauty obliterated all other considerations, and was in fact the answer to those questions which we bundle under the head of Truth, should have been in the slightest degree disturbed by the discovery of the dispersion of light as exhibited by the rainbow. It would be absurd to quote seriously a remark dropped between drinks at a dinner party, such as the idea that 'Newton had destroyed all the poetry of the rainbow by reducing it to its prismatic colours'; but Keats did elaborate the charge in *Lamia II* with the lines:

> Do not all charms fly
> At the mere touch of cold philosophy?
> There was an awful rainbow once in heaven:
> We know her woof, her texture; she is given
> In the dull catalogue of common things.
> Philosophy will clip an Angel's wings,
> Conquer all mysteries by rule and line,
> Empty the haunted air and gnomed mine—
> Unweave a rainbow . . .

That is a real 'murder to dissect' attitude. In passing, we may wonder what Shelley thought of those lines. For Shelley loved science and was greatly influenced by astronomy and attracted to chemistry. 'It symbolizes to him joy, and peace, and illumination,' says Whitehead. 'What the hills were to the youth of Wordsworth, a chemical laboratory was to Shelley. It is unfortunate that Shelley's literary critics have, in this respect, so little of Shelley in their own mentality. They tend to treat as a casual oddity of Shelley's nature what was, in fact, part of the main structure of his mind, permeating his poetry through and through. If Shelley had been born a hundred years later, the twentieth century would have seen a Newton amongst chemists.' That is a good gambit: and we are bound to admire that 'would have'. He goes on to illustrate the permeation of Shelley's poetry by science by giving as example 'the vaporous exultation not to be confined' as the exact poetic transcript of 'the expansive force of gases'; followed by eight lines of extraordinary support for six lines of extraordinarily weak verse. His claim is somewhat dubious, just as it is dubious to suggest, as others have, that Shelley's 'The Cloud' could not have been written without a knowledge of meteorology, or his lines, 'Life like a dome of many-coloured glass, Stains the white radiance of Eternity,' without benefit of Newton's prism. However, Whitehead's main point is that Shelley who was so sympathetic to science and absorbed in its ideas was not in the smallest degree influenced by the doctrine of secondary qualities which had made Blake so angry. He simply ignored it.

I do not think that Keats was distressed by what Locke or Descartes had to say, he may not have read them. But he does appear to have been bothered by Newton's explanation of colours and hence of the rainbow. He has unwoven it, Keats says; he has taken it to pieces; he has dissected it. Therefore he has murdered it. Its beauty is gone. It is now in the dull catalogue of common things. But why? (And is any common thing really dull?) This is an odd point of view for a poet. I take it that my own point of view is the more normal: I rejoice at the red of the rose. Then I am severely told that nothing is red. I am told that no colour is 'a fact in external nature'. I am told that redness is merely motion of material; that the light striking my eyes is merely motion of material; that sound striking my ears is merely motion of material; that scent striking my nostrils is merely motion of material. I am told that without eyes, ears, or noses there would be no colour, sound, or scent in the universe. I am supposed to be depressed. But I am easily pleased. I had thought that the redness belonged to the rose—and I was glad. I am now told that it was eight minutes ago in the sun—and again I am glad, since this strikes me as being even more miraculous. Colour may not be strictly a 'fact'. It is allowed to be an 'event'. It remains a reality: and not less a reality because my own mind helps to shape it. The rainbow is still a rainbow 'considered by the theologian to be a wonderful sign of God and by the scientist to be a sign of the Laws governing God's creations,' as Spinoza said.[1] When we are told new things about Nature our sense of wonder is increased not decreased. When we learn about colours we do not thereby think that the holy chalice of the yellow tulip is less pure a cup; that the candelabra of the chestnut trees burn with less bright a flame; that the peacock is robbed of its prodigy of plumage; nor fail to see Stevenson's 'ragged moor receive The incomparable pomp of eve'.

iv

SCIENCE AND IMAGINATION

I think we are inclined to become enslaved by categories.

[1] *Reeckering van den Regenboog* in *Opera Quotquot Reperta Sunt.*

We imagine we are imprisoned behind barriers that do not necessarily exist. Thus we speak of the scientific approach over against the poetic approach to reality, and of the analytical mind over against the creative mind, and of reason against intuition. It is true that these faculties are realities. It is true that there is the knowledge which comes with ecstasy and the knowledge which comes with rational effort. There is the way of analysis and there is the way of imagination. But one lot does not exist in this kind of person and the other lot in that kind of person. Most of us use both and they are not in neat packets in our heads either. Consider. I sit in the garden under a pear tree. I see an animal in front of me in the air. It is not a bird, it has no wings, it cannot fly; but it is getting on extremely well, and has comfortably taken a seat upon nothing. By way of experiment I give it a little prod, and at once it rises as if in a lift to a twig above my head. Presently it comes down in the lift again. And as I gaze at this creature we call a spider I see that it puts up as good a show as anything to be seen on earth. Now what has been my attitude, my approach? Have I been scientific or poetical? Have I bestowed the analytical or imaginative faculty upon it? I don't know. Quite honestly, I don't mind. The probability is that I have used an amalgam of all the faculties I possess in my endeavour to really see the little creature.

I do not think we can put the true scientist on the left and the true poet on the right and think of them as in different categories. They are in the same category: they are both artists. In both the main faculty is imagination. Imagination is the power to see what is there. Once an agricultural labourer said to me after an aeroplane had crashed in an adjoining field: 'It wouldn't do for anyone as has too much imagination to go over and look at it, for he might be seeing things as aren't there.' But that is what imagination is *not*. It is the power to see what is there. Fancy, invention, is the capacity to see what is not there. Imagination sees what is there with full concentration in combination with the faculty of love—indeed imagination has also been defined as 'Intellectual Love' and as 'Reason in her most exalted mood'. This is man's highest faculty, the power to see, to be a seer, to fasten upon the total significance of phenomena—and even to image further. It was by his 'wonderful imagination', we are told, that Newton was constantly discerning new tracks and new processes in the region of the unknown. This imaging into the centre of reality seems to belong to the great scientists as much as to the great poets. There is nothing to choose here in force of imaginative power between a Rutherford who can penetrate into the very heart of matter and a Tolstoy who can penetrate into the very heart of man.

The distinction between science and art is 'purely conventional' said Herbert Spenser, 'for it is impossible to say where art ends and science begins'.[1] The learned historian of science, Charles Singer, defined it as 'knowledge in the making' and as 'the growing edge between the unknown and the known'. That is to say it is active and creative, essentially artistic. We are not talking about the man who applies science over against the creative artist, but of two sorts of artist. It has been claimed, surely with truth, that there is no such thing as 'an unimaginative scientific man'. John Tyndall said of Faraday that 'the force of his imagination was enormous', and it has always seemed to me that Tyndall himself was a good example on a lower plane; he says how he could hardly sustain with any degree of calmness the beauty of phenomena revealed by his physical

[1] His essay, 'The Genesis of Science'.

researches. 'The true spirit of delight,' said Bertrand Russell, 'the exaltation, the sense of being more than man, which is the touchstone of the highest excellence, is to be found in mathematics as surely as in poetry'—more so perhaps, judging from some modern poets.

Sometimes it is far from certain whether we should call a given man a scientist or an artist. Ruskin claimed to possess the most analytical mind of his time. He is thought of as an art-critic, I believe. He was primarily a geologist who liked painting. His own drawings seem to me wonderful, and at times he was a great poet in prose: in few men have science and literature been so integrated, however undisciplined and unwhole his individual books. When we think of Leonardo da Vinci we do not know what to call him. Indeed his case is still held over. It is not yet decided whether he should be called the supreme painter of his day or the supreme scientist. Some have suggested that it is almost as plausible to regard Leonardo as primarily an engineer as primarily a painter. 'The dispute as to whether he was above all an artist or a man of science is a foolish or even an unmeaning dispute,' wrote Havelock Ellis, himself an example of the artist integrated with the scientific investigator and philosopher. He thinks that Leonardo's painting was only a concession to his age, and that from youth to old age he had directed his whole strength to one end: the knowledge and mastery of Nature. The medium in which he worked was Nature, the medium in which the scientist works; 'every problem in painting was to Leonardo a problem in science, every problem in physics he approached in the spirit of the artist.' Finally, Havelock Ellis compares him with Newton: 'He seemed to himself to be, here and always, a man standing at the mouth of a gloomy cavern of Nature with arched back, one hand resting on his knee and the other shading his eyes, as he peers intently into the darkness, possessed by fear and desire, fear of the threatening gloom of the cavern, desire to discover what miracle it might hold. We are far here from the traditional attitude of the painter; we are nearer to the attitude of that great seeker into the mysteries of Nature, one of the very few born of women to whom we can ever passingly compare Leonardo, who felt in old age that he had only been a child gathering shells and pebbles on the shore of the great ocean of truth.'[1]

It is true that Newton did not appreciate art in the restricted sense and declared that sculpture was no better than the making of stone dolls. It is true that Darwin in his *Autobiography* lamented his increasing incapacity to endure a line of poetry, and said that when he tried to read Shakespeare he found him so intolerably dull that he was nauseated. It is sad, of course, that Newton and Darwin were so narrow in their approach, but this has little to do with our present proposals. 'Darwin was one of those elect persons', to quote Ellis again, 'in whose subconscious, if not their conscious, nature has implanted the realization that science *is* poetry, and in a field altogether remote from the poetry and art of convention he was alike poet and artist.' Such a remark could be easily misinterpreted and still more easily misapplied, but personally I would accept it heartily, for I really do think that it is maddening nonsense to suppose that the shaper and creator of thought is less of an artist than the creator of design. The trouble arises owing to the existence of the bogus gentlemen. There are many who claim the title of scientist without any right to it— men who are mere compilers of facts. These people are no more loved by genuine scientists than the mere bookmakers cluttering up the literary scene (men who in happier

[1] *The Dance of Life.*

days, before ignorance and illiteracy had made such rapid strides, would have been peacefully employed in copying illuminated MSS.) are loved by genuine literary men. These 'scientists' are always the first to decry and even to prove the 'impossibility' of imaginative proposals such as the introduction of the telegraph, or the telephone, or the airship, or the steam locomotive, and so on. These are the people who do actually approach reality in a completely analytical and abstracting manner which spells death to the quality and value of the thing-in-itself, so that, for example, as Eddington pointed out, an elephant sliding down a grassy hillside on to a bed of softly yielding turf becomes 'a mass of two tons' sinking 'at an angle of 60°' on to 'a coefficient of friction'.[1] Pointer-readings take the place of the reality (or poetry) of the object just as to a musketry instructor that tree on the hill is simply 'a definite object' to be fired at. These are the people who, habitually exercising their minds in this manner, do really come to believe that knowledge is a question of weighing, measuring, and counting. They even become unaware that the object's property of quality is its chief truth for humanity at large. If you argue with them they tell you that you are 'emotionally involved' as if that proved something against you. Their pointer-readings are skilful and useful, but the habitual attitude of mind engendered weakens their intelligence. It is low grade when off the speciality—not much above that of a garage assistant. When they write they do so without personal touch or quality, so that if one has to review a symposium of their essays, there is no distinguishing one from another. Actually, they despise language. They do really think that instead of saying, 'Let there be light', it would be better to say, 'Let the molecules swing together

[1] Eddington: *The Nature of the Physical World*, pp. 251-3.

effectively.' They feel that that is being tough and hard-boiled. It is indeed: but it is the toughness of over-cooked beef; it is the hard-boiledness of an overdone egg—in both cases indigestible.

The truth is that from early youth they have been forced to concentrate upon the part. In the end they are never able to see the whole. A man has a better chance if he first attains a vision of the whole and then comes to the part. Still, I must add that, in my experience, many young scientists are not content with their partiality and show an interest in the humanities. They compare favourably with the literary men who take pride in asserting that they 'don't know a thing about science'.

v

GOETHE'S ATTACK ON NEWTON

At this point the reader may feel inclined to ask how, if there is no conflict between the true scientist and the true poet, it came about that Goethe carried on a feud against Newton for thirty years? Since Goethe is perhaps the most celebrated name in literature for combining poetic sensibility with an absorbed interest in science, this conflict may seem a little odd. It might be thought that the child who was thrilled with Franklin's doctrine of electricity and that the man who, among other scientific interests and experiments, proposed a botanical theory on the metamorphoses of plants, would have been at ease with Newton. Yet it is not so strange, for the fact is that he was too much at ease and felt confident that he knew better. He did have something of the greatest importance to say. His method of doing so, however, was curious, and was not free from some slight element of comedy.

From early youth Goethe had enjoyed theorizing on painting, though he could not paint (it was unnecessary for him to theorize on poetry). So he came to colour. What is colour? He was referred to Newton. One day Professor Büttner lent him some prisms and optical instruments to carry out the prescribed experiments. He put off using them. It is rather strange, this. The great poet and science student for months was too slack even to take a prism in his hand. He was repeatedly asked to return the equipment, and at last received a definite demand that they must be returned at once. So he roused himself, took one prism and looked through it at the white wall of his room. He expected to see, and according to the rules he thought he should see a rainbow-coloured wall. But he did not. The wall remained white—with coloured edges. The experiment had failed to work for him. Immediately he exclaimed aloud: '*Newton's theory is false!*'

It is rather interesting. Newton, the acknowledged supreme intellect of the seventeenth century, after endless labour had interpreted the heavens and examined the constitution of light, and for nearly a hundred years his theory had stood the test. Then Goethe glances through a prism for a few minutes, fails to see what he expects, and instantly declares that Newton is wrong. The plain truth is Goethe had all the arrogance of the man of position and reputation. We are reminded of Tolstoy; or rather, of Tolstoy in his old age as seen by Chekhov. 'All great sages', said the latter, 'are as despotic as generals, and as ignorant and indelicate as generals, because they are confident of impunity. Diogenes spat in people's beards fully aware that he would not be punished for it. Tolstoy abuses doctors as scoundrels and allows himself to remain in ignorance of great questions because he is just such a Diogenes who won't be taken to the police-court nor be abused in the papers.'[1] So with Goethe. Newton had got it all wrong. He had perpetrated an experimental incoherence. To try to analyse light was a shallow blunder. To suppose that white light could contain coloured light or that when coloured rays were squashed together they would look white, was to suppose an absurdity, to indulge in fairy-tales. To pass a poverty-stricken thread of light through a tiny hole into a dark room, when by going out into the open air any amount of it could be had free of charge, was ridiculous. He elaborated his own *Theory of Colours*. Colours originate, he said, in the modification of light by outward circumstances. They are not developed *out* of light but *by* light. For the phenomenon of colour there is required darkness as well as light. (Personally, I can get the colours without any darkness in the bright spray giving me my rainbow in the garden.) That was the gist of his Theory. He never looked back. His was 'the pure doctrine'. His opponents were simply people who 'continued in error'. All that was necessary to understand it was 'a sound head'—in contradistinction to the imperfect intelligence of Newton. He repeatedly told Eckermann that he took no pride for what he had done as a poet, but that in his century he was the only person who knew the truth in the difficult science of colours—of that he was not a little proud. He had come into a great inheritance: Napoleon had inherited the French Revolution; Luther had inherited the darkness of the Popes; and he had inherited the errors of the Newtonian theory.

Now I have no intention whatever of spoiling my book

[1] Chekhov: *Letters.*

at this stage by being drawn into this controversy on the physics of light. In any case I do not possess the equipment. It also seems clear that Goethe himself did not know much more about physics, *per se*, than he did about ornithology (remember his endearing remark to Eckermann that he could not distinguish a lark from a finch). No layman can move freely in the field of light-dispersion without detailed study—let alone propose a theory of his own. When I first acquainted myself with this business of Goethe and the prism I thought it only sensible to conduct the same experiment myself and find out what I personally saw on looking through a prism at a white wall. I did so in my own room; and I saw—*exactly what Goethe saw*: a white wall with coloured edges. I was neither pleased nor sorry. But I went a step further than Goethe. I stepped into the garden. I hung a white towel on the laundry line. Standing three yards away I looked at it through the prism. Again I saw what I had seen in the room. Then I retreated thirty yards distance from the towel and looked at it once more. This time it was *fully rainbowed* except for a little white in the middle.

Even if I could I would not, here, go into the reasons for this—reasons which are explained by Newton in terms of 'pure and impure spectra'. For I do not mind about it. If I were obliged to teach anyone anything or pass any examinations, I would mind—otherwise I prefer to let it go. You may think that my refusal to worry further in this matter exhibits a deplorably unscientific frame of mind. Yet, speaking quite personally—but hoping that I am speaking for some others as well—I have now enough here to nourish the imagination. That is the motive of my studies. Carlyle offended Ruskin by going to North Wales for two months 'and noting absolutely no Cambrian thing or event, but only increase of Carlylian bile'.[1] I am not as bad as that. Carlyle also pained Darwin by saying that 'he thought it a most ridiculous thing that anyone should care whether a glacier moved a little quicker or a little slower or moved at all'.[2] In fact he could not care less. I could not agree more— *au fond*. For though I happen to have studied the glacier question carefully and the controversies about it, I really do not care a bit about the rate of movement. Science helps us to see more in a given thing than we would otherwise see; it puts us through the discipline of factual concentration, which is the best possible way to feed and enrich the imagination. In my own case when it has once done this I am satisfied and can dispense with further facts and controversies. So with the theories of colour: I confess that I am supremely indifferent as to whether colours arrive *in* the light or *by* the light; it is the fact that they have arrived at all that holds me; it is in the finished article that I am finally interested. Perhaps some of my readers may agree with me, and they may wonder why Goethe was so concerned with the mechanism of the business; they may wonder what philosophical or religious significance the actual mechanism could possibly have for him or anyone else.

That brings me to my main point, and my reason for introducing this controversy at all. For Goethe feared that the scientific descriptions of mechanism would promote a philosophy of mechanical materialism. He put forward his views without the force of economy, without wit, without grace, and without clarity—yet he has found support from that day to this. He was hailed by Hegel, by Schelling, and later by Schopenhauer who wrote an elaborate defence of

[1] Letter to E.N.C.
[2] Darwin's *Autobiography*.

his theory,[1] while in our own day he has received the massive support of the great Rudolf Steiner who attacked the new physics in a manner fully as puzzling but much more amusing: 'The theory of the colour of solids', he writes, 'is worthy of the new physics. Why is a body red? A body is red because it absorbs all other colours and reflects only red. This is the explanation so characteristic of the new physics, for it is based approximately on the logical formula: Why is a man stupid? He is stupid because he absorbs all cleverness and radiates only stupidity outwards. If one applies this logical principle so common in colour-theory everywhere to the rest of life, you see what interesting things result.'[2] But he does not say why anyone else should wish to apply this principle to the rest of life, or why it is wrong to apply it to colour.

It may give some of us on this side of the Channel pleasure to turn for light to our own dear Coleridge who was kind enough to separate the threads. 'If it please the Almighty to grant me health, hope, and a steady mind,' he wrote to Poole on 23 March 1801, 'before my thirtieth year I will thoroughly understand the whole of Newton's works. At present I must content myself with endeavouring to make myself entire master of his easier work, that on Optics. I am exceedingly delighted with the beauty and neatness of his experiments, and with the accuracy of his *immediate* deductions from them.' That is a pleasing approach to Newton, and we are the more ready to attend to his criticism. He goes on: 'But the opinions founded on these deductions, and indeed his whole theory is, I am persuaded, so exceedingly superficial as without impropriety to be deemed false. Newton was a mere materialist. *Mind*,

[1] *Van der Farben* in *Schriften zur Erkemmtmiblehre* (1873).
[2] *Colour.*

in his system, is always *passive*—a lazy *Looker-on* on an external world. If the mind be not *passive*, if it be indeed made in God's Image, and that, too, in the sublimest sense, the *Image of the Creator*, there is ground for suspicion that any system built on the passiveness of the mind must be false, as a system.'[1]

We can all rejoice in the beautiful mechanism of optics. The whole vegetable world has no eyes, can see nothing of its own beauty. Some animals have no sight: to this day the worm, for instance, is without eyes and would not know what to do with a pair. However, in the course of evolution the bodies of most animals became sensitive to radiation and the molecules responded in a special manner to light-waves. As time went on and larger animals developed they lost the sensitivity to this force over the whole body and concentrated it in a particular place—a little patch sensitive to light. This patch grew into a sense organ entirely responding to light. After countless ages it evolved into the Eye—serving alike the girl who also speaks (or listens) with her eyes and for the rattlesnake's deadly cleft in the glazed blue of the ghastly lens; for eyes perched on pyramids of bone or waving on the vulnerable points of the snail's pillars; for eyes brandished on horns or massed in clusters.

We can go inside an eye and have a look round just as if we were entering a room. In fact the way to do this is by entering a room. We go in, shut the door, and pull down the blinds. Opposite the window we put up a white screen. Rude as this equipment is, it is all we need in order to sit inside an eye. We need only do one other thing—make a little hole in the middle of the blind, and take a seat in a corner of the room. Then immediately, because light is not something stationary, because it is the arrival, the con-

[1] Letter XLVI in the Nonesuch *Coleridge*.

tinuous arrival of energy, it forces its way through the little hole in the blind. If outside the window there are a tree, a cottage, a pond, a field, and a man, all scattering the rays of the sun, then from every part of those objects rays will pass and print themselves upon the screen—and we have a *picture* of the scene outside. We are sitting inside a camera, however crude. We are sitting inside an eye, however rudimentary. For room read dark walls of camera; for screen read photographic plate; for blind read shutter; for hole read lens. And then for walls of camera read walls of eye; for photographic plate read retina; for shutter read iris; for lens read eye.

(In parenthesis: it seems strange at first that instead of the little round hole in the blind being printed on the screen, the whole scene outside should manage to make its way through the opening. Luckily we need not take this second-hand: we can prove it for ourselves without any laboratory. Thus I take the tray out of an empty match-box, stick some white paper across the open side, pierce a hole with a needle through the middle of the bottom of the tray— opposite the white paper—and then hold that side up close to the flame of a candle in the dark. And there on my screen is an image of the candle-light—but hundreds of times larger than the needle-hole through which it passed. The light has not been in the least concerned by the small- ness or shape of the opening—the whole thing has easily got through. But it is upside-down on the screen. The reason for this also explains the reason for its being there at all. We must never think of light as a stationary thing, but as straight-lined rays advancing from every bit of the object at which they are being scattered. Thus the image is bound to be upside-down, for (see diagram) the arrow passing its rays through the hole must send them as shown.

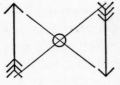

Instead of thousands of rays I have shown exactly two, the last ray from the extreme point of the arrow, and the last ray from the extreme end of the tail. If a screen obstructs the rays before they get diffused, and the hole is smaller than the arrow, then the point of the arrow is bound to be at the bottom instead of the top.)

Light, then, being a succession of waves in swift movement, enters the eye at the rate of so many million vibrations a second. Let us go back to the first primitive movement. It was made in response to chemical action upon the light-sensitive single-celled body. When the creature evolved more cells some responded to light while others were alone capable of movement. A communication cord linked them. This cord, or nerve, conducted an electric current as a message from the light-sensitive part demanding muscular expansion and contraction in the cells capable of movement. So what we have got here is—first, the vibrations beating upon the eye, and second the nerve-conductor which communicates the message to the third thing, a muscle ready for action. As the animals developed in the course of evolution a network of conductors came into existence, and the centre of this system, the brain, sorts out the messages and governs instantaneous action.

We use a term for this, a well-worn term now—we call it reflex action. It implies something purely mechanical. *It promoted a philosophy of mechanism.* It seemed possible to be able to eliminate the necessity for a spiritual principle. The fact that I see a red tulip in the garden can be given a purely physical explanation. I am not really seeing the tulip over there: I am not really looking at it—there is simply an image of a tulip in my head. How did it get there? It was excited into existence by vibrations or agitations working upon the material substance of my brain; these motions were set going by previous vibrations on the optic nerve; these by previous vibrations in the eye; and these by previous vibrations in space.

That is the upshot of the policy. You may feel inclined to say that this is absurd and that I am tilting at windmills. True, it is against the experience of mankind. But that does not prevent learned men from making the deduction and proposing a philosophy of mechanism. It is one of the many clever ways of being stupid. And just as thousands of modest men are easily floored by humbug and cant, not being able to detect these as such, so their sense of reality is easily clouded by determinists. A great physiologist once said to Ruskin that sight was 'altogether mechanical'. Ruskin comments that the words meant, if they meant anything, 'that all his physiology had never taught him the difference between eyes and telescopes. Sight is an absolutely spiritual phenomenon; accurately and only, to be so defined: and the Let there be light, is as much, when you understand it, the ordering of intelligence as the ordering of vision.'[1] Any ordinary person with an unclotted and inquiring mind (such as my own if I may say so) who goes to Optics to find out what *luminosity* is, why it is that we see *light*, gets no answer; nor does he receive any answer as to how vibrations can be ordered into images unless there is an agent inside our heads capable of doing it—a Mind, a Spiritual Apparatus at work. Given the lens there still must be an active and not passive mind at work over and above the machinery. 'It is the appointment of change', Ruskin says again, 'of what had been else only a mechanical effluence from things unseen to things unseeing, from stars which did not shine

[1] *The Eagle's Nest.*

to earth that could not receive; the change I say of that
blind vibration into the glory of the sun and moon for
human eyes.'

This may seem fairly obvious. Yet the melancholy fact
remains that many of us when we are shown a mechanism
conclude that it is only a mechanism. It is as if on my
showing some one a watch he were to say that it had no
spirit. But it has a spirit. It is bound to have a spirit in the
form of a general maker and winder-up. The tendency to
emphasize the mechanical at the expense of the spiritual
seems to be a perennial danger and existed long before the
modern age. 'If now someone should ask you', says Socrates
to Theætetus, 'by what does a man see white and black
objects and by what does he hear shrill and low sounds, I
suppose you would say, by eyes and ears.' Theætetus assents
and Socrates continues, 'A careless ease in the use of names
and expressions without pedantic linguistic analysis is for
the most part not ignoble. The opposite is rather the mark
of a mind enslaved. But sometimes it is necessary to be
more exact. For example, it is necessary now to consider in
what respect the answer you have given is incorrect.
Reflect: which answer is more correct, eyes are that *by*
which we see, or that by means of which *we* see, and ears
that *by* which we hear or that by means of which *we* hear?'
Theætetus answers, 'It seems to me, Socrates, truer to say,
by means of which than *by which* we perceive in each case.'
'Yes, indeed,' says Socrates, 'for it would surely be a
terrible thing if so many powers of perception were seated
in us like warriors in wooden horses, and if all these senses
did not draw together into some one form, call it soul or
what you will, by which, using these senses as instruments,
we perceive whatever we do perceive.'

It was necessary to say this in the days of Plato. It is

necessary to say it today; for commenting upon that very passage, Dr. H. G. Wood in the 1957 Eddington Memorial Lecture, adds: 'I cannot see that this analysis is outmoded, or if it be outmoded I think it is still sound. It is truer to say that we see by means of our eyes than that our eyes see. And though the relation of ourselves to our brains is more intimate than the relation of ourselves to particular powers of perception such as eyes and ears, yet in this case, if the question is put, Do our brains think, or do we think by means of our brains? I should plead for the second alternative.' It was necessary for Coleridge to say the same thing before him. It was necessary for Goethe to say it at the time when it seemed that the new science was making it plausible to refer everything to mechanical and chemical reactions, and the perception of colour to be merely an automatic response of matter whether external to man or within the eye and brain. He may have spoilt some of the force of his affirmation by dogmatic assertions and physical caveats; he may have over-stepped the mark in speaking of Newton's 'empirico-mechanico torture chamber' and in declaring that he must rescue mankind from 'the pathology of experimental physics'; yet he was surely right in accusing the physicists of the day of subjectivity, of 'an excessive emancipation of the subject from a totality of which it is a mere part';[1] he was surely right in conceiving Mind as something in us not wholly *ours*, independent of whether we want it or not, a part of Nature playing its role within us as upon a stage, and subjective only in as much as it makes its appearance within us and thinks through our help; and he was surely right in repeating over and over again the dictum of Plotinus: 'If the eye were not sun-like

---

[1] Erich Heller's 'Goethe and the Idea of Scientific Truth' in *The Disinherited Mind*.

how could we ever see light? And if God's own power did
not dwell within us how could we delight in things divine?'

Goethe loved to personify Nature—quite in the old
pagan manner. His response was such that he could not
avoid it. Even when a boy, after listening to too much
theological discussion amongst his family he would go to
his bedroom, make an altar from a music-stand, deck it
with minerals and flowers, and crown it with a flame lit by
a burning-glass from the rays of the risen sun. His apostro-
phies to Nature are well-known. It is not strange that such
a man would react as violently as Blake to the abstractions
of Descartes and Locke. We must remember that these poets
were eighteenth-century men reacting to the new thing.
The first reactors are always the most violent. Think of the
violence of the first reactors to industrialism!

Yet there seems to be confusion as to the final upshot
of what was being put forward. In an often quoted passage,
Whitehead outlines the theory of primary and secondary
qualities as proposed by Locke and Descartes. Thus mass
with definite location was a primary quality, while colour
or scent or sound are secondary qualities not actually
belonging to the given mass. Then he goes on: 'Mental
apprehension is aroused by occurrences in certain parts of
the correlated body, the occurrences in the brain for instance. But the mind in apprehending also experiences
sensations which, properly speaking, are qualities of the
mind alone. These sensations are projected by the mind so
as to clothe appropriate bodies in external nature. Thus the
bodies are perceived as with qualities which in reality do
not belong to them, qualities which in fact are purely the
offspring of the mind. Thus nature gets credit which should
in truth be reserved for ourselves; the rose for its scent: the

nightingale for its song: and the sun for its radiance. The poets are entirely mistaken. They should address their lyrics to themselves, and should turn them into odes of self-congratulation on the excellency of the human mind. Nature is a dull affair, soundless, scentless, colourless: merely the hurrying of material, endlessly, meaninglessly.' However this may be disguised, says Whitehead, this is the practical issue of the scientific philosophy which closed the seventeenth century and was carried on into modern times. 'And yet', he adds, 'it is quite unbelievable. This conception of the universe is surely framed in terms of high abstractions, and the paradox only arises because we have mistaken our abstraction for concrete realities.'[1]

Apart from the fact that probably not one single person has ever taken the abstraction for the concrete reality, there seems some lack of fusion here—at least I find it confusing. For that philosophy, if taken on its own ground, should not upset anyone. Note that Mind is by no means excluded. On the contrary it is represented as doing a big job. If we strip the passage of its rhetoric we find that Whitehead is simply saying that the mind is largely responsible for harmonizing our stream of impressions into a glorious picture. Now if this is really so and that we thus make sense out of otherwise senseless vibrations, why should the poets not do us some odes upon the excellence of the human mind? We still have the thing in itself, the finished article.

Goethe said that it was no use trying to wrest the truth of Nature by using the screws and levers of science—we can only get at the facts that way. To get at the truth, the significance, the quality, we need another instrument. The spanner we need for that is imagination. Science deals with how things are assembled, imagination with the value and

[1] *Science and the Modern World.*

significance of the assembly. The same man ought to be able to use both tools. When we use the latter we do not abstract all but the vibrations, we contemplate the thing itself: and then—what a difference! Colour, for instance, seems to have nothing to do with theory or controversy, and shines before us as the most powerful and the most redemptive of all the servants of beauty.

vi

ENLIGHTENED MEN

We come to a final consideration. Literature and Scripture is riddled with the symbolism of Light. Hymns, sermons, poems, rituals, exhortations, prayers are laden with metaphors of light. In fact there is too much of it: we weary of so much illuminated metaphor. Sometimes it is used as more than metaphor. When it is said that God is love it is a statement rather than a metaphor. So also with God is light. The terms seem almost interchangeable. 'Since God is light,' said Milton, 'And never but in unapproached light Dwelt from Eternity'—it was 'Bright effluence of bright essence increate'. We turn to the religion of the Zoroastians who were said to take stars for money rejoicing at seeing something they could not put into their pockets: for them the vital principle of their religion lay in the recognition of one supreme power, the God of Light, in every sense of the word. We turn to the Koran. 'God is the LIGHT of the Heavens and Earth,' runs Sura XXIV. 'Light is like a niche in which is a lamp—the lamp encased in glass—the glass, as it were, a glistening star. From a blessed tree is it lighted, the olive neither of the East nor of the West, whose oil

would well nigh shine out, even though fire touched it not!
It is light upon light.' We turn to the Bible. 'God is light
and in Him is no darkness at all'; 'I am the light of the
world'; and of course the many exhortations—'Walk in
the light', 'Let your light so shine before men', 'Believe in
the light', and 'In thy light we shall see light'.

It scarcely matters whether all this is metaphor or not,
since a metaphor is such a profound thing. Light is the
term used to denote spirit. It is also the term used to
embrace matter. 'We have come into the possession of a
wonderful principle,' says Bragg, 'which unites all forms of
radiation and all forms of matter. We may rightly speak of
light as constituting the Universe.' Certainly religion and
science come very close together here. The outer light and
the inner light may be different aspects of the same thing.
Since this would be merely an intellectual synthesis I do
not know that I would bother to mention it were it not
for the existence of a more compelling sign concerning
the spiritual nature of light. I refer to the illumination—
in two senses—which so often accompanies the mystic
experience.

The mystic experience. This is surely the only ultimate.
A mystic, however much and however often the word may
be abused, should be defined as the man who is no longer
mystified—by religions, by theologies, by doctrines, by
formulations. He is at ease with religions, having attained
Religion: he is no longer diseased by overdoses of doctrine.
He occupies this favourable position by virtue of his
experience which brings with it such joy and such certainty
that he no longer needs dogmas about salvation: this
experience to him is salvation. He no longer needs to solve
the lesser problems: they have been dissolved. It may not
last for more than a few minutes but it changes the man's

outlook for ever—*he has seen the light*. These men are our true leaders; their goal of higher consciousness our chief hope. Their message comes down the years always with the same power to convince, always undated and undating. Their words bring continual support to the whole and the happy, and they bring hope and healing to the unhappy, to the broken in heart and even in purse, to the doubtful and to the dying.

This crucial experience is often accompanied by intense inner illumination. Yet the accent is not on the inner but on the illumination: it just is *light*. It matters little where we turn for examples since whatever source we take them from they are equally convincing. 'Light untellable', says Whitman, 'lighting the very light'—he who, unlike most mystics, dwelt for long periods on this plane though in a quiet way. George Fox, terribly compelled, indeed propelled, by his inner voice, tells how he found himself immersed in an ocean of light. We know how Wordsworth expressed it, as the poet's additional gleam, the consecration, 'the light that never was on sea or land'. We recall the simple words of Havelock Ellis—'I trod on air, I walked in light.' We think of the pathetic and terrible cry of A. J. Symonds—'It is too horrible, it is too horrible, it is too horrible!' For when he was under chloroform he had an ecstatic vision of God. 'I felt him streaming in like light upon me . . . I cannot describe the ecstasy I felt.' Then he awoke from the influence of the anæsthetics and the vision went. It was intolerable. He could not bear it. 'Why did you not kill me? Why would you not let me die?' he shrieked at the frightened surgeons. He felt he had been tricked. Since the psychic experience had come to him through the physical loosening caused by the drug, he thought, as a man taking mescalin might think, that the experience itself was therefore suspect.[1] In *My Quest for God* J. Trevor tells how on one brilliant Sunday morning he felt he could not accompany his wife and children to chapel but must remain on the hills—he felt that it would be spiritual suicide to go down. So, reluctantly and sadly, he parted from his wife and boys and went further up into the hills with his stick and his dog. 'In the loveliness of the morning, and the beauty of the hills and valleys,' he says, 'I soon lost my sense of sadness and regret. For nearly an hour I walked along the road to the "Cat and Fiddle" and then returned. On the way back, suddenly, without warning, I felt that I was in Heaven—an inward state of peace and joy and assurance indescribably intense, accompanied with a sense of being bathed in a warm glow of light, as though the external condition had brought about the internal effect—a feeling of having passed beyond the body, though the scene around me stood out more clearly and as if nearer to me than before, by reason of the illumination in the midst of which I seemed to be placed.' In his book called *Cosmic Consciousness* which has been an inspiration to many, R. M. Bucke describes how he returned home one evening after talking with friends. He says he was in a quiet and passive mood. 'All at once without warning of any kind I found myself wrapped in a flame-coloured cloud. For an instant I thought of fire, an immense conflagration somewhere close by in that great city; the next I knew that the fire was within myself. Directly afterward there came upon me a sense of exultation, of immense joyousness accompanied or immediately followed by an intellectual illumination impossible to describe. Among other things I did not merely come to believe, but I saw that the universe is not composed of dead matter, but is, on the contrary, a living Presence.'

[1] *The Varieties of Religious Experience.*

The utterances of these enlightened men brings me to the end of this book on light, which, starting with physics, ends quite naturally with metaphysics. In between I have described certain phenomena, hoping that though little can be explained about any thing, we may come to see that it IS—and we can scarcely go deeper than the Biblical words, I AM THAT I AM. Perhaps we solve the riddle of the world by being able to see the world. Why lose our one chance to see it? What shall it profit a man if he lose the whole world without any guarantee that he has gained his soul? If we use *all* our faculties, little will seem commonplace, much may be transfigured. I have sought to do no more than take a mirror, wipe it, and place it in your hands.

Bibliography

Abetti, G., *The Sun*, Lockwood, 1938.

Andrade, E. N. da C., *The Atom and its Energy*, Bell, 1947.

——, *The New Chemistry*, Bell, 1936.

——, *Modern Physics*, Bell, 1956.

——, *Sir Isaac Newton*, Collins, 1954.

Anthon's *Classical Dictionary*, Everyman.

Baker, Henry, *The Microscope Made Easy*, 1670.

Beebe, W., *Adventuring with Beebe*, Bodley Head, 1956.

——, *Half Mile Down*, Bodley Head, 1940.

Bonner, J. and Galston, A. W., *Principles of Plant Physiology*, Freeman, San Francisco, 1952.

Bowen, E. J., *Chemical Aspects of Light*, Clarendon Press, 1942.

Bragg, W. H., *The Universe of Light*, Bell, 1947.

Broglie, Louis de, *The Revolution in Physics*, Routledge & Kegan Paul, 1954.

Browne, Thomas, *Religio Medici*, 1643.

Bucke, R. M., *Cosmic Consciousness*, Philadelphia, 1905.

Carpenter, Edward, *Pagan and Christian Creeds*, Allen & Unwin, 1920.

Cheskin, L., *Colours. What They Do for You*, Liveright, N.Y., 1947.

Coleridge, S. T., Nonesuch Edition, edited by Stephen Potter.

Cox, George, *The Mythology of the Aryan Nations*, 1882.

Darwin, Charles, *Autobiography*, Watts, 1929.

——, *The Movements of Plants*, Murray, 1880.

——, *The Voyage of the Beagle*, Everyman.

Dingle, Herbert, *Modern Astrophysics*, Collins, 1924.

——, *The Scientific Adventure*, Putnam, 1952.

Duggar, Benjamin, *Plant Physiology*, Macmillan, 1911.

Eckermann, *Conversations with Goethe*, Everyman.

Eddington, A. S., *The Expanding Universe*, C.U.P., 1933.

——, *The Nature of the Physical World*, C.U.P., 1928.

Eddington, A.S., *The Philosophy of Physical Science*, C.U.P., 1949.

Ellis, Havelock, *The Dance of Life*, Constable, 1923.

Evans, Ifor, *Literature and Science*, Allen & Unwin, 1954.

Fabre, J. H., *The Heavens*, Fisher Unwin, 1924.

——, *The Wonder Book of Plant Life*, Fisher Unwin, 1924.

Finberg, J. G., *The Atom Story*, Wingate, 1952.

Fiske, J., *Myth and Myth Makers*, Boston, 1873.

Frazer, J. G., *The Dying God*, Macmillan, 1936.

——, *The Magic Art*, Macmillan, 1936.

——, *Balder the Beautiful*, Macmillan, 1936.

Freeman, A., *Goethe and Steiner*, Sheffield Educational Settlement, 1947.

Fritsch, F. E. and Salisbury E., *Plant Form and Function*, Bell, 1946.

Gamow, George, *The Birth and Death of the Sun*, Macmillan, 1941.

——, *Atomic Energy in Cosmic and Human Life*, C.U.P., 1947.

——, *Mr. Tompkins Explores the Atom*, C.U.P., 1945.

Gasset, Ortega y, *The Revolt of the Masses*, Allen & Unwin, 1951.

Goethe, W., *Theory of Colour*, tr. Eastlake, Murray, 1840.

Gunther, K. and Deckert, K., *Creatures of the Deep Sea*, Allen & Unwin, 1956.

Hammer, C., *Goethe After Two Centuries*, State University Press Louisiana, 1952.

Hardy, A., *The Open Sea: the World of Plankton*, Collins, 1956.

Hartridge, H., *Colours and How We See Them*, Bell, 1949.

Harvey, E. N., *Living Light*, Princeton, 1940.

Hecht, Selig, *Explaining the Atom*, Gollancz, 1955.

Heller, Erich, *The Disinherited Mind*, Bowes & Bowes, 1952.

Hooke, Robert, *Microphalia*, 1660.

Hoyle, Fred, *The Nature of the Universe*, Blackwell, 1950.

Hughes-Gibb, E., *The Life Force in the Inorganic World*, Routledge & Kegan Paul, 1930.

Humboldt, Alex von, *Aspects of Nature*, Murray, 1849.

Jacks, L. P., *Near the Brink*, Allen & Unwin, 1953.

James, William, *Varieties of Religious Experience*, Longmans, 36th Impression, 1928.

Jeans, James, *The Universe Around Us*, C.U.P., 1945.

——, *Physics and Philosophy*, C.U.P., 1948.

Johnson, Amy, *Sunshine*, 1892.

Jones, G. O., Rotblat, J., and Whitrow, *Atoms and the Universe*, Eyre & Spottiswoode, 1956.

Lehns, Ernst, *Man or Matter*, Faber, 1951.

Lewes, G. H., *Life and Works of Goethe*, Everyman.

Luckiesh, M., *Artificial Light*, University of London Press, 1920.

MacDougal, D. T., *The Green Leaf*, New World of Science Series, Appleton-Century-Crofts, 1930.

Mann, Ida, and Pirie, A., *The Science of Seeing*, Penguin Books, 1946.

Massey, H. S. W., *Atoms and Energy*, Elek Books, 1953.

Meyer, B. S. and Anderson, D. B., *Plant Physiology*, Chapman & Hall, 1940.

Milton, John, *Paradise Lost*.

Minnaert, M., *Light and Colour in the Open Air*, Bell, 1940.

Nature, Vol. 150, 1942.

Newton, Isaac, *Optics*, Modern Edition, Bell, 1931.

Nicolson, Marjorie, *Newton Demands the Muse*, Princeton, 1946.

——, *The Microscope and English Imagination*, College Studies in Modern Languages, Vol. 16, No. 4.

——, *The Telescope and Literature*, Studies in Philology, Vol. XXXII, 1935.

O'Dea, John, *Darkness into Daylight*, Science Museum.

——, *The Social History of Lighting*, Routledge & Kegan Paul, 1958.

Olcott, W. T., *Sun Lore in All Ages*, Putnam, 1914.

Pascal, Blaise, *Pensées*.

Peattie, Donald C., *Flowering Earth*, Phoenix House, 1948.

Phipson, T. L., *Phosphorescence*, 1870.

Physical Society, *Proceedings*, Vol. LV, 1943.

Pope, Alexander, *Essay on Man*, 1733.

Roberts, Michael, and Thomas, E. R., *Newton and the Origin of Colours*, Bell, 1934.

Robins, John, *The Story of the Lamp*.

Rogers, F. and Beard, A., 5000 *Years of Glass*, Lippincott, N.Y., 1948.

Ruskin, John, *The Eagle's Nest*, 1870.

——, *Ethics of the Dust*, 1866.

Russell, Bertrand, *The ABC of Atoms*, Routledge & Kegan Paul, 1924.

Sachs, F. G. *The Physiology of Plants*, Clarendon Press, 1887.

Saunders, B. C. and Clark, R. E. D., *Order and Chaos in the World of Atoms*, English Universities Press, 1942.

Schindler, Maria, *Goethe's Theory of Colour*, Steiner Book Centre.

Scoresby, W., *The Arctic Regions*, 1820.

——, *Observations on a Greenland Voyage*, 1810.

Shelford, B., *Curiosities of Light*, 1899.

Sherrington, Charles, *Goethe on Nature and Science*, C.U.P., 1949.

Steiner, Rudolf, *Colour*, Steiner Book Centre.

Sullivan, J. W. N., *Isaac Newton*, Macmillan, 1938.

——, *The Physical Nature of the Universe*, Gollancz, 1932.

——, *Science, a New Outline*, Nelson, 1935.

Timiriageff, C., 'The Cosmical Function of the Green Plant', *Proceedings*, Royal Society, 72, 424–61: 1903.

Tyndall, John, *Six Lectures on Light*, Longmans, 1895.

——, *Notes on Light*, Royal Institution, 1869.

Weil, Simone, *The Need For Roots*, Routledge & Kegan Paul, 1952.

Whitehead, A. N., *Science and the Modern World*, C.U.P., 1926.

Wigglesworth, V. B., 'The Light of Glow-worms and Fire-flies', *Science News 11*.

Wilson, M., *What is Colour?*, Goethean Science Foundation, 1949.

Index

Adams, George, 119, 137

Air, solid; living substance created from, 32; invisible solids in, 43–6; forming bubbles, 57–8

Alchemical reaction, 19–22

Anaxagoras, on sun, 123

Andrade, E. N. da C., 7

Animals; dependence on plants, 34–5; phosphorescence in, 76–79; development of response to light in, 158, 160

Argon, 16

Art and science, 136–7, 148–50

Atom, 5–8; combinations of, 6, 16–17, 51; division of, 9–10; structure of, 10–12; coherence of, 14–15; splitting the, 18–21; source of light, 22, 51

Aureole, 46

Aurora Borealis, 46

Bacon, Roger, 110, 112, 115

Bacteria, luminous, 76–7, 79; discovery of, 120

Barytine, 68–9

Bathysphere, 38, 82

Beebe, William, 38

Beryllium, 16

Bethe, Hans, 25

Blake, William, 139–41, 164

Blueness of sky, 44–5

Bologna stone, 68–9

Boyle, Robert, 118

Bragg, Sir William, 44, 142, 167

Browne, Sir Thomas, 117, 137

Brownian Movement, 8*n*.

Bubbles, 57–61

Bucke, R. M., 169

Burning-glasses, 62

Calorescence, 70

Camera, 111, 159

Candle, 88–9; flame of, 51

Carbon, 25, 30–1, 33

Carbonic-acid gas in atmosphere, 34–5

Carboniferous forests, 18, 34

Carlyle, Thomas, 155–6

Cascariola, Vincenzo, 68–9

Catalysts in solar energy, 25

Caves, vegetation growing in, 33; reflection in water in, 55–6; phosphorescence in, 75

Chekhov, 153

Chemical reaction, 18, 22; sun's rays producing, 30; producing flame, 51–2

Chlorine atom, 16

Chlorophyll, 31

Christmas Day, 130–1

Clouds, shaft of sun through, 44; iridescent, 46, 60; luminous, 73

Coal, energy from, 18, 20; latent energy in, 77

Coal mine, fish 'lamps' in, 76–7

Cockcroft, Sir John, 19

Coleridge, S. T., 157, 163

Colours, 35–43; of flowers, 35, 37; of spectrum, 36–7; in depths of sea, 38, 82; as seen through prism, 40–3, 155; of sky, 43–6; of soap-bubble, 59–60; explanation of mechanism of, and poetry, 136, 144–6; Goethe's theory of, 154–7

Combination of atoms, 6, 16–17, 51–2
Combustion, 51–3
Corona, 46
'Corpse-candles', 72
Cowley, Abraham, 137
Cucujo beetle, 77–8
Cyclotron, 19

Darwin, Charles, 80–1, 150
Desert mirages, 64, 66–7
Devil-fish, deep-sea, 83
Dew-bow, 46
Dingle, Herbert, 143
Donne, John, 138–9
Drops, 61–2; of water acting as prisms, 36–7, 46, 47, 62; acting as burning-glass, 62; acting as magnifying-glass, 63

Earth, origin of, in sun, 22; before organic life, 33–4
East, solar significance of, 131
Eddington, A. S., 24, 151
Eddystone lighthouse, 89, 94
Egyptian solar religion, 123, 132–133
Einstein, Albert, 20
Electric light, 93–4; bulb, 96–7; in churches, 102
Electricity, 4; and atom, 11, 15; and spirit, 142; nerves as conductors of, 160
Electrons, 11–12, 15–17
Elements, 6; radioactive, 9; combinations of, 14–17; stable and unstable, 15; transmutation of, 19
Ellis, Havelock, 149–50, 168
Energy, sources of, 3–4; manifested by motion, 8; released by chemical action, 17–18, 51; nuclear, 19–21; equals mass, 20; solar, 23–7; stellar, 39
Explosives, 18
Eyes, 158–60

Finnish sun-legends, 128
Fire, 49–53; energy from, 3; 'catching', 17
Fire-flies, 78–9
Fish, used as lamp, 76–7; deep-water luminous, 83–4
Flame, 49–52
Flower colours, 35, 37
Fluorescence, 71
Fluorine atom, 16
Focus of rays, 62
Fog, luminous, 72–3
Fog-bow, 46
Fox, George, 168
Fox-fire, 75
Fungi, phosphorescent, 74–5, 80

Galileo, 111–13
Gamow, Dr. George, 5, 7, 12, 25
Gases, combustion of, 4, 92; noble or inert, 16
Gas-light, 92
Geophysics, 39–40
Glass, 105–6; houses, 108–9; mirror, 109–10; lenses, 110–11; stained, 120
Glow-worm, 77, 99
Goethe, J. W. von, his attack on Newton, 139, 152–5, 163–5; colour theory of, 154–7; fears philosophy of mechanism, 156, 163
Greek sun-myths, 123, 125–6, 134

Halo, natural phenomenon, 46; saint's, 132
Haydon, Benjamin, 136

Heat, 28, 49–50; waves, 29, 49
Heilgenschein, 46
Helium, 23–6
Helmholtz, Hermann von, 23
Hercules, solar symbolism of story of, 126
Hiroshima, 21, 39
Hooke, Robert, 117, 137
Hydrogen, 24; atom of, 11; transformed into helium, 23, 25–6

Ice, making fire from, 63; demonstrating crystals of, 64
Ignis Fatuus, 72
Imagination, 147–8; and science, 146–66
Inert gases, 16
Infra-red rays, 49; calorescence of, 70
Insects, luminous, 77–9, 80
Iridescence, 60–1

Jack-o'-Lantern, 72
Jeans, Sir James, 13, 24, 26

Keats, John, on Newton, 136, 144–5
Krakatoa, eruption of, 45–6

Lamb, Charles, 88*n*., 136
Lamp, fish used as, 76–7; first, 89–90; fat-, 90; stormy petrel used as, 90; oil-, 90–2; arc-, 93; carbon filament, 94, 96–7; discharge, 97
Leaf, photosynthesis by, 31–2, 35
Leeuwenhock, Antony van, 117, 119–20, 137
Lens, burning-glass, 62; in demonstrating ice-crystals, 63; glass, 110–11; of eye, 161
Leonardo da Vinci, 92, 149–50

Light, source of, 22; impact of, 26, 29; nature of, 28–53; speed of, 28; photosynthesis of, 31–2, 35; and colour, 36–9; diffraction of, 46; refraction of, causing mirages, 63–7; in depth of sea, 82–4; basis of matter, 142–143; development of animal response to, 158, 160; symbolism of, 166–7; mystic experiences of, 167–70
Lighting, development of, 87–104; gas, 92; electric, 93; neon, 97; of rooms, 97–8; of factories, 99; horrors of bad, 100–104; street, 102–4
Lightning, 17
Limestone, phosphorescence of, 69–70
Lithium, 16, 19
Living light, *see* Phosphorescence
Looming, 65–6
Luminescence, *see* Phosphorescence

Magnifying-glass, 63, 110
Materialism, mechanical, 156
Matter, energy stored in, 4; divisibility of, 6
Mechanism, philosophy of, 156, 160–6
Melville, Herman, 73–4
Meteorological phosphorescence, 72
Microbiology, 120
Microscope, 115–20
Milton, John, 113–15, 166
Mind and mechanism, 161–6
Mineral phosphorescence, 68–71; oil, 90–1
Minnaert, M., 45
Mirages, 63–7

Mirror reflections, 54–5, 109–10

Molecules, 6–7; of air, 44–5; movement of, and heat, 50

Moon, blue or green, 45; in mythology, 127

Mother-of-pearl, 60–1

Murdock, William, 92

Mystic experience, 167–70

Neon atom, 16; light, 97

Neutrons, 11

Newton, Isaac, colour discoveries of, 35–6, 153; poets and, 136–145; *Optics* of, 138, 157; imagination of, 148; Ellis on, 149–50; Goethe's attack on, 152–5, 163–5; Coleridge on, 157–8

Nitrogen, 25

Noble gases, 16

Noctiluca Millaris, 80–1

Norse sun-legends, 128

Nothingness, mystery of, 13–14

Nuclear: physics, 4–5; energy, 19–21; war, 21–2; reactions in sun, 23–7

Nucleus of atom, 11–12; 'splitting' the, 18–21

Observatory, 133

Oil, energy from, 18; -lamps, 90–92

Optics, mechanism of, 158–60

Oxygen atom, 16; released by plants, 31–2, 35

Pascal, Blaise, 116

Pelican eel, 84

Pepys, Samuel, 137

Periodic Table, 15

Phœbus Apollo, 123

Phosphorescence, 68–84; in minerals, 68–71; in air, 71–4; in plant, 74–6; in animals, 76–79; in sea, 80–4

Phosphorus, 69

Photosynthesis, 32

Planets, discovery of, 111

Plants, use of carbon by, 30–2, 34; use of water by, 33; mutual dependence of animals and, 34–45; phosphorescent, 74–6

Poetry and science, 136–45, 147, 152

Pope, Alexander, 138–9

Prism, colour demonstrated through, 36, 40–3; Goethe and, 153–5

Protons, 11

Radiations, solar, 26, 29, 70–1; source of colour, 35–7; stellar, 39

Radioactivity, 9, 18

Radium, 15, 20

Rain, luminescent, 71–2

Rainbow, 47–8; home-made, 36; Keats and, 136, 144–5

Raleagh, Lord, 44

Reflection, 54–7; of colour, 37; mental, 57; in mirage, 64; law of total internal, 66

Reflex action, 160

Religion, sun in, 122–35; light and, 166–70

Royal Society, The, 137

Rushlight, 88

Ruskin, John, 149, 155, 161

Russell, Bertrand, 15, 149

Rutherford, Lord, 6, 9–10, 19, 148

St. Elmo's Fire, 73–4

Salt, 16

Science, and awareness, 133–5;

and art, 136–7, 148–50; poetry and, 136–45, 147, 152; and imagination, 146–70

Scientists, imagination of, 147–150; bogus, 150–2

Scoresby, W., 65–6

Sea, energy from, 22; colour changes in depths of, 38; looming phenomenon at, 65–6; mirages seen at, 66; light phenomena seen at, 73–4; phosphorescence in, 80–4; oil derived from organisms of, 90–1

Sea-worm, polynoid, 83–4

Shelley, Percy Bysshe, 144–5

Silver, stability of, 15

Singer, Charles, 148

Sky colours, 43–6

Snowflakes, luminescent, 71–2

Soap-bubbles, 58–60

Socrates, 162

Sodium atom, 16

Solar wheel, 131–2

Space, proportion of solid to, in atom and universe, 12–13; realization of interstellar, 112–114; Pascal on, 116

Spectacles, 110

Spectroscopy, 39

Spectrum, 36–7; invisible colours of, 49; 'pure and impure', 155

Spenser, Herbert, 148

Splinter, 88

Stars, radiations of, 39

Steiner, Rudolf, 157

Street-lighting, modern, 102–4

Sun, source of energy, 22–6; losing bulk, 26–7; rays of, 29, 70–1; source of colour, 35; composition of, 40; shaft of light from, 44; spots and prominences on, 46, 134; worship of, 122–35; Anaxagoras's theory of, 123; legends and myths of, 123–9; relics of worship of, 130–2; as Hell, 134

Sun-gods, 122–4, 130, 132–3

Sunset colours, 45–6

Surface tension, 62

Swastika, 132

Swift, Jonathan, 119, 138–9

Symonds, A. J., 168

Telescope, 111–15

Thomson, James, 138

Thunderstorms, atmospheric phenomena associated with, 71–4

Tolstoy, Leo, 148, 153–4

Torch, 88

Transparency, 105–6

Trees, atmospheric purification by, 34

Trevor, J., 169

Tyndall, John, 59, 148

Ultra-violet rays, 49; fluorescence of, 70–1

Universe, emptiness of, 13, 14

Uranium, 9, 11, 15, 20, 22

Vegetation, use of light by, 30–2; growing in dark, 33. See also Plants

Venetian glass, 106

Water, energy from, 3, 18; plants' use of, 33; producing fire, 52; reflections in, 55–7; air-bubbles in, 57–8; seen in mirage, 64–5, 67; seen under microscope, 119–20. See also Drop

Weizsacher, Dr. Carl von, 25

Whale oil, 90

Whitehead, A. N., 142, 144–5, 164–5
Whiteness, 38–9
Whitman, Walt, 168
Wilkins, John, 118, 137
Will-o'-the-Wisp, 72
Windows, 105–7; tax on, 107; stained-glass, 120–1
Winter solstice, 129–30

Wood, phosphorescent, 75, 80
Wordsworth, William, 136, 141–142, 168

Yule log, 131

Zeta, 22
Zoroastrian religion, 166